W9-AVG-289

THE MERIDIAN BOOKS

HOW WARS ARE FOUGHT
The Principles of Strategy and Tactics
By CAPTAIN J. E. A. WHITMAN

CODES AND CIPHERS
By ALEXANDER D'AGAPEYEFF

SECRET SOCIETIES
By D. W. PIKE

MAPS

By

ALEXANDER D'AGAPEYEFF

AND

E. C. R. HADFIELD

OXFORD UNIVERSITY PRESS
LONDON NEW YORK TORONTO

PRINTED 1942 IN GREAT BRITAIN BY RICHARD CLAY AND COMPANY, LTD.,
BUNGAY SUFFOLK

INTRODUCTION

THE two authors of this book have each had a different experience of maps : for while one made them, the other, in a secondhand bookshop off the Charing Cross Road, sold them, and through his hands passed maps of most of the great map-makers, or cartographers, of the world—Mercator, Ortelius, Blaeu, Saxton, Speed, and many others.

It is said of Richard Hakluyt, the author of the famous book of Elizabethan Voyages, that he was drawn to the study of geography and voyaging by seeing a map of the world, and so " waded still farther and farther in the sweet study of cosmographie ". Perhaps all of us have been thrilled by maps of the world, have pored over atlases or " dusty maps of Mexico, dim as dreams, and soundings of the bay of Panama ", or have paused in the street to look at some old map in a bookseller's window.

This book attempts to deal with as many different aspects of the subject as can be got into the pages. The authors hope that it will lead readers, on the one hand to take more interest in the ordinary maps that they see and use in atlases or in the series published by the Ordnance Survey, on the other to collect some of the old maps, whether of English counties or foreign countries that can be found quite cheaply in bookshops, or to study them in any other way that takes their fancy. They know that once the fascination of maps has been felt, many happy hours can be spent by anyone with or without much money to spend.

At the end of the book will be found a list of books on maps, and the authors wish to express how deeply they are indebted to all of them. Any of these works can be obtained without cost through the public library system, and any collector would do well to look through Mr. T. Chubb's great book, *The Printed Maps in the Atlases of Great Britain and Ireland*, and to read and master every word of Sir G. Fordham's little book called *Maps, their History, Characteristics, and Uses*.

It may be thought that in the historical chapters there are too many names and dates ; yet no name has been mentioned which is not well known, and whose maps are not in some way remarkable, while dates have been given so that the events we describe may be brought into proper relation with contemporary happenings. History, sometimes so seemingly dull, gains much in vividness and interest if it can be seen in its linking-up with a specialised subject like maps.

Lastly, the authors wish to acknowledge their debt to Mr. G. M. Pitt for his assistance with the first six chapters; to Lieut.-Commander R. Birch, and to Mr. H. J. W. Wilson, librarian of the Paddington Borough Libraries, without whose help the authors, while each engaged in war work, could not possibly have written this book; and to Major W. L. Melville Lee for reading the proofs and making numerous valuable suggestions, and for the loan of maps from his collection.

A. d'A.

E. C. R. H.

CONTENTS

LIST OF PLATES

ACKNOWLEDGMENTS

The thanks of the publisher are due to Messrs. Thomas Nelson & Sons for permission to include the illustrations of Cosmas' Map (p. 85), the Turin Map (p. 86), and the Anglo-Saxon map (p. 88), and to quote the description of them, from 'A Book of Discovery' by M. B. Synge; and to Messrs. Maggs Bros., Ltd., for the loan of John Speed's Map of Middlesex (Plate 3), and the blocks of Ptolemy's Map (Plate 1), and Wagenar's Chart of the Thames Estuary (Plate 6). The section of the modern Admiralty Chart (Plate 7) is reproduced by permission of the Controller of H.M. Stationery Office and of the Hydrographer of the Navy.

CHAPTER ONE

DISTANCE

THE purpose of the first six chapters of this book is to throw light upon the mysteries of map-making, so that when using a map the reader will appreciate it better. To most people a map conveys no vivid picture : it is something to consult when a motor-car or bicycle journey is intended, or when one has lost the way.

Into the making of a map goes much labour, backed by long experience. Upon a single sheet is drawn a great deal of information, which brings to the mind a picture more complete than any book could give.

The ability to read a map is possessed by most people in greater or less degree, but there is much ignorance of how the surveyor gets to work, and how long distances, the shape of hills, and directions of rivers, roads, and railways are determined. This knowledge is not necessary before one can use maps, but the more one uses them the more one wonders by what means a representation of the earth's surface, or part of it, can be so conveniently drawn on paper.

To describe the surveyor's methods it is best to take his problems one by one. The first is how to measure distance in the field and how it can be represented on a sheet of paper.

Scale. The ratio existing between lengths on the map and lengths on the ground is the scale, and when making a map this depends upon how much of the earth's surface has to be represented, and how large a sheet of paper will be used for the purpose. An atlas map of Europe, for instance, may be on a scale as small as 1 inch to 300 miles. Sometimes the degree of detail to be shown limits the extent of the earth's surface which can be represented. The very excellent English Ordnance Survey maps, with a scale of 1 inch to the mile, are detailed enough to show footpaths, parish boundaries, farms, etc., but for this to be possible the total area of England has to be divided up and shown on many separate sheets. Still greater detail is shown on the 6-inch-to-the-mile and the 25-inch-to-the-mile Ordnance Survey Plans, but the extent of territory shown on one sheet is correspondingly smaller in each case.

When the scale is expressed as a fraction, it is called the Representative Fraction, or R.F., thus :

$$1 \text{ in. to } 1 \text{ mile } = 1 \text{ in. to } 63{,}360 \text{ ins. } = \frac{1}{63{,}360} = \text{R.F.}$$

$$6 \text{ ins. to } 1 \text{ mile } = 6 \text{ in. to } 63{,}360 \text{ ins. } = \frac{1}{10{,}560} = \text{R.F.}$$

$$1 \text{ in. to } 2 \text{ feet } = 1 \text{ in. to } 24 \text{ ins. } = \frac{1}{24} = \text{R.F.}$$

$$1 \text{ in. to } 100 \text{ links } = 1 \text{ in. to } 792 \text{ ins. } = \frac{1}{792} = \text{R.F.}$$

$$1 \text{ cm. to } 1 \text{ km. } = 1 \text{ cm. to } 100{,}000 \text{ cms. } = \frac{1}{100{,}000} = \text{R.F.}$$

The advantage of expressing the scale as the Representative Fraction, rather than as so many of one kind of unit to so many of another, is that it is understood in all countries.

Thus the International Map of the world, upon which the work of production sheet by sheet is still going on, has a scale of $\frac{1}{1{,}000{,}000}$ or $1/\text{M}$, as it is more generally written, which is more convenient than expressing it as 1 inch to 15·782 miles, for a foreigner might not be familiar with our units of measurement.

In order that the reduction of measurements taken in the field to their scale values may be fully understood, let us make a plan of a room.

Suppose the room to be a rectangular one 20 feet long and 15 feet wide, and that we have to make our map upon a sheet of paper 12 inches square. A convenient scale is ½ inch to the foot, which will give a plan 10 inches long by 7½ inches wide. Notice at once that the Representative Fraction is $\frac{1}{24}$. In order to save numerous mathematical calculations of lengths on the map to represent distances in the room, it is best to construct what is called a Plain Scale, from which lengths can be taken directly with a pair of dividers and measured on the plan. This is done by drawing a straight line on the paper where it will not be in the way of the plan, and it is better for its length to be not less than 6 inches. It should be of an exact length that can easily be divided into scale

units, and as our units are half inches, we will
make it exactly 6 inches long. The line must
then be divided into half inches to represent
feet, and the first half inch on the scale we
divide into twelve, to represent inches in the
room.

Now to plan the room.

We measure one of the longer walls, and
find its length to be 20 feet. This, reduced
to scale, will be exactly 10 inches long, so we
draw a line of that length across the bottom of
the paper to represent that wall. All subsequent planning will be done with that line as
a base, so it is called the Base Line. Measurement of one of the shorter walls gives a length
of 15 feet to be represented on the plan, and,
as the room is rectangular, we erect a perpendicular 7½ inches long to one end of the
base line. All further measurement will be
made directly or indirectly from these two
lines, which are called the Co-ordinates of the
plan.

There is a golden rule of planning and map-
making, which is always to construct first a
framework and then fill in the detail. Surveyors work from the whole to the part, never
the other way about. Never build a map by
adding little bits until you complete the area.
Consider the whole area to be the framework,
and add detail to that.

With this in view, we measure and draw
the other walls first, and then measure the
distances from the walls to objects in the room,
always making measurements from the co-
ordinate walls, or from objects already plotted
by measurement from them.

The Plain Scale from 0 to 11 represents
a distance of 11 feet, so that when a distance
of 11 feet or less has to be shown on the plan,
a pair of dividers is used to find the exact
scale-length required. The divisions on the

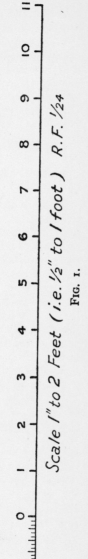

Scale 1" to 2 Feet (i.e. ½" to 1 foot) R.F. ½4

Fig. 1.

first half inch are of use when the length measured in the room is so many feet and so many inches.

Gradually the detail of the plan will appear within its rectangular framework, just as the roads and streams, fields and farms, appear on the map made by the Ordnance Surveyor. The latter has greater distances to measure, sometimes making necessary expensive instruments and more complicated methods, but there is a distinct relationship between planning a room and mapping a country.

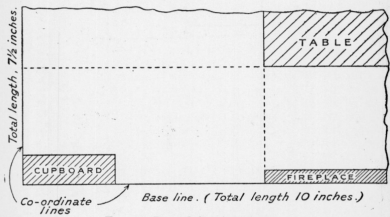

FIG. 2.—Part of the plan of a room.

When planning irregularly shaped fields, it might at first seem difficult to imagine a framework into which detail can be added, but the surveyor does this by dividing up the ground into large triangles.

Fig. 3 shows a field to be surveyed. It is by no means regular in shape, and cannot be planned in the same simple fashion as the room. Yet by its division into the triangles *ABC*, *ADB*, and *FDE*, a framework is constructed about which the curves and details of its hedges can be drawn by the use of offsets, which will be explained later. The triangles are chosen to include as much of the field as possible, and the sides are taken as near to the sides of the field as is convenient.

In order to measure accurately distances such as the length

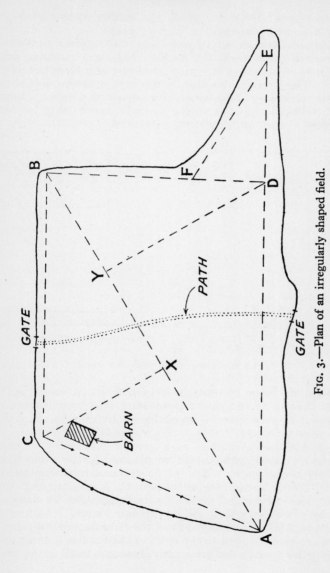

FIG. 3.—Plan of an irregularly shaped field.

of the sides of these triangles, a surveying chain, known as Gunter's Chain, is used. This is 22 yards long (the length of a cricket pitch), and is composed of 100 steel links, at the ends of which are two handles. With each chain ten arrows, made of iron or steel, are provided, to be used as will be described. For longer distances a chain of 100 feet is used, and the two are known as the Short Chain and the Long Chain, to distinguish them.

Notice that the chain and the link are each units of measurement :

$$
\begin{aligned}
\text{100 links} &= \text{1 chain.} \\
\text{10 chains} &= \text{1 furlong.} \\
\text{8 furlongs} &= \text{1 mile.} \\
\text{10 square chains} &= \text{1 acre.}
\end{aligned}
$$

When measuring the triangle dimensions, the chaining is done by two people, the " leader " and the " follower ". All the corners of triangles are marked with surveyor's staffs, and the follower holds the handle of his end of the chain so that it touches Staff A on the ground. The leader walks in the direction of B, carrying his end of the chain and the ten arrows. When the chain is taut the leader turns and faces A, while the follower aligns him on the staff marking B. The first arrow is then pushed into the ground to mark the end of the chain. The follower walks up to this position and places his handle to the arrow, while his partner walks on towards B. The operation is repeated, the follower picking up each arrow as soon as measurement is completed from it, until B is reached. The odd links are counted, and the arrows used are formally handed over to the leader. The total distance from A to B will then be as many chains as there were arrows used, plus the odd links.

The arrow method of counting chains is quite essential, for without them it would be too easy to miscount the number of times the operation was carried out.

By the same method all the other triangle sides are measured, and the record made in a note-book. A rough plan of the field and its triangles may be made by the surveyor during the work, as an aid in the construction of the accurate plan which will be done subsequently in the drawing office.

When making the plan the draughtsmen first decide on the scale, and construct a plain scale, as we did when planning the room. The position of point A on the paper is plotted, and the line AB drawn to the correct scale length. With a pair of compasses the scale length for AC is taken off the plain scale, and an arc inscribed about A as shown in Fig. 4. The scale length of BC is also taken off the plain scale, and with centre B an arc is drawn to cut the first arc at C. The triangle ABC on the paper will then be a scale plan of the triangle ABC in the field, and the other triangles can be

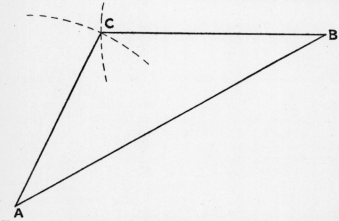

FIG. 4.—The plotting of triangles by the use of intersecting arcs.

plotted by the draughtsmen in the same way to complete the framework.

It will be clear that the nearer to 45° the angles CAB and ABC are, the more accurate will be the plotted position of C, and this should be remembered when dividing the field into triangles at the beginning of the survey. Triangles which give a small chance of error when plotting the position of the apex by drawing arcs about the ends of the base-line are called Well Conditioned. In all work based on intersection of arcs, the surveyor tries to make his triangles as well conditioned as possible.

There is a surveyor's instrument called an Optical Square

or Cross Staff, which might be used in a survey such as this,
but a simple device which would serve the purpose can be
made by fixing a flat square of wood horizontally on top of a
camera tripod. Two lines crossing each other at right angles
are drawn on the little table so formed, and a nail is driven
in at each of the four ends, as in Fig. 5.

This is used when making measurements at right angles
to the Gunter's chain as it lies on the ground. For instance,
if, while originally chaining AB, it were to occur to the
surveyor that the perpendicu-
lar measurement to C might be
useful when later checking the
plotted position of that point,
he would wait until he had
reached a point on AB that
looked perpendicularly opposite to C. He would align the
sighting nails P and Q of his
cross-staff on the points A and
B, and move up or down the
chain lying on the ground until
he could see the point C in
alignment with the nails S and
R. He would mark that position X with a stick or sur-

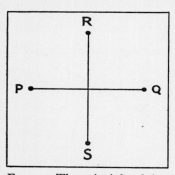

Fig. 5.—The principle of the
optical square or cross-staff.

veyor's staff, and at some convenient time later chain CX. If
the distance were not long enough to justify chaining, it
should be measured immediately with a separate measuring
instrument, the surveyor's tape, and the record made in the
note-book.

The note-book used in surveying is a specially prepared one
with long pages opening vertically away from the user.
Each page has a vertical column ruled down the middle, and
the book is begun at the bottom of the last page (Fig. 6).

The first entry made in any particular survey will be details
of place and time, showing what is being surveyed and when
the work was done. The next will be the letter denoting the
starting point, ringed round, as a rule, to show that it is a
station from which measurement will be made, and placed
within the column in the centre of the page. All distances
chained in a forward direction are recorded in this column

upwards from the letter showing the starting point. The finishing point is entered as a second ringed letter, and a line is drawn right across the page to denote that measurements below relate to one and the same straight line, and that measurements above relate to a straight line in another direction. The space on either side of the central column is used to record information, such as the rough direction of roads or paths crossed whilst chaining, and the distances measured with the tape to points along hedges, fences, walls of buildings, etc., so that the position of these can be plotted by the draughtsman about the triangular framework of his plan.

These distances, measured at right angles to the chain as it lies on the ground, are called offsets.

Let us return to the surveying of the irregular field, and see how entries are made in the Field Note-book, neatly and methodically, to provide the draughtsmen with full particulars for completing their work.

The first entry in the note-book column will be a ringed A, for the chaining is to be done from A to B. The distance in links to X, the point to which the check line from C will be measured, is entered next, and beside it, in the space to the left of the column, will be shown a dotted line indicating the direction of the check line to C. Its length will not be recorded here, unless it is measured immediately, in which case the figure of its length will be written beside the dotted line.

A path is the next feature to be met while chaining, so that the next entry in the column will be the distance from A to the path, with a little drawing of its rough direction appearing both to the right and left of the column. The point Y, from which a check line to D might eventually be measured, can be found with the cross staff and marked with a surveyor's staff. Its distance from A is entered in the column, and the direction of D denoted on the right. The distance of A to B is the next entry, followed by a ringed B, and a line drawn right across the page.

Then we proceed to chain BC, so we begin with a ringed B. Now, the hedge near BC is straight, so that if we take two offsets to it, the correct position can be plotted on the plan later. The first should be taken at B, so a nought goes in the column to indicate no distance along the chain from B, and

B

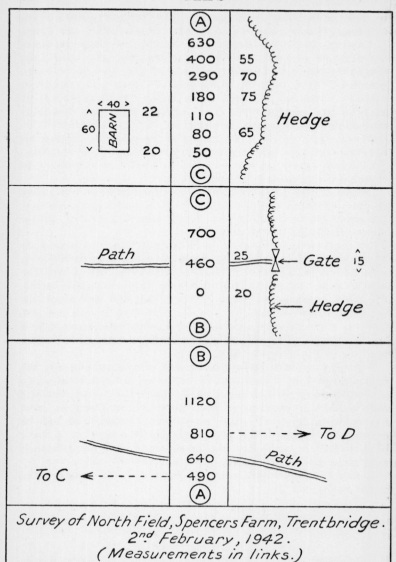

	Ⓐ	
	630	
	400	55
	290	70
	180	75
˄ < 40 > 22	110	*Hedge*
60 BARN	80	
˅ 20	50	65
	Ⓒ	

	Ⓒ	
	700	
Path	460	25 ◁▷ ← *Gate* ˄15˅
	0	20 ← *Hedge*
	Ⓑ	

	Ⓑ	
	1120	
	810	- - - → *To D*
	640	*Path*
To C ← - - - - -	490	
	Ⓐ	

Survey of North Field, Spencers Farm, Trentbridge.
2nd February, 1942.
(Measurements in links.)

Fig. 6.—Page of Field Note-Book showing how record is kept of
chained distances and offsets.

we put the distance to the hedge beside it, on the right of the column. Whilst chaining along *BC* we cross the path again, put the distance from *B* in the column, draw a little sketch of the path on each side, measure the offset to the gate and put the offset measurement to the right of the column. A little sketch of the gate, with its length, is put in its appropriate place, with the direction also of the hedge. Point *C* is reached, and the total distance *BC*, together with a ringed *C*, entered, and a line drawn across the page.

When sketches of detail on either side of the column are necessary to help the draughtsman, only the bare essentials are shown, such as the rough shape and direction; the sketches are not drawn to scale.

When chaining along *CA* more frequent offsets are required to determine the position of the hedge, because it is curved, but they are entered in the same methodical way on the appropriate side of the column, against the distance chained from the starting point. When buildings are present, such as the barn near *C*, offsets are taken to the nearer corners, the dimensions measured with the tape, and recorded in the same way as other offsets. The work goes on around and across the field until each triangle is completed, and from the methodical record of the note-book the draughtsman will have no difficulty in first constructing his scale framework of triangles, and later filling in the detailed shape and other features of the irregular field.

It might seem that the description of a simple survey has been unduly long, but it is deliberately detailed and described at length because the use of triangles, offsets, and the field note-book is a characteristic of plan and map-making that has to be understood before more complicated work can be examined. Indeed, once the principles described so far have been firmly grasped, the understanding of more advanced map-work is comparatively easy.

Before closing this chapter, however, it is necessary to mention the following :

Horizontal Equivalent. When measuring distances on sloping ground, the distance chained from one point to another is the ground surface or sloping distance, not the horizontal equivalent distance that has to be recorded on a plan or map. If, for instance, we were walking in very hilly or mountainous country, like that of Scotland, and had to cross a deep valley with steep sides from *A*, high up on one hill, to *B*, the same height on the hill opposite, the distance we would have to walk down one hill and up the other would be much farther than the straight line across from *A* to *B*. The straight-line

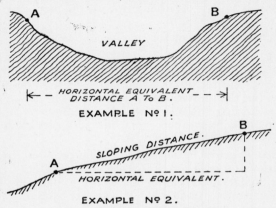

FIG. 7.—Horizontal equivalent.

distance is the horizontal equivalent, and this is the distance that would appear on the map.

In most cases, however, slopes are only gentle ones of a few degrees, and the surveyor is able to reduce his slope distance to its horizontal equivalent by merely deducting a proportion based on the angle of incline. We can measure the latter with an instrument called the Clinometer, which we shall explain later on.

Table for Converting Sloping Distance to Horizontal Equivalent

Angle of Incline to the horizontal.	Gradient.	Percentage to deduct from sloping distance.
7½	1 in 8	1
12	1 in 5	2
14	1 in 4	3
16	1 in 3½	4
18	1 in 3	5
20	1 in 2¾	6

Limitations of Scale. Not all features represented on a plan or map can be drawn exactly to scale, because there is a limit to the fineness with which a line can be drawn on paper. A road, for instance, shown on an inch-to-the-mile map may in actual fact be 30 feet wide. Now, the Representative Fraction of this map is $\frac{1}{63,360}$, so that a line on the map representing the correct scale width of the road would be $\frac{30 \times 12}{63,360}$, or $\frac{1}{176}$ inch thick, which is very fine indeed. Imagine how fine a line representing a pathway would have to be to show the correct scale width. Such accuracy is neither possible nor necessary, but the limitations of scale should be borne in mind when map-reading. Roads, pathways, streams, etc., are shown by convenient conventional signs, not scale drawings, unless the scale is very large.

Accuracy Required in Surveying. The previous paragraph on limitations of scale has a bearing on surveying. If roads, pathways, hedges, etc., can be shown on a map only by conventional signs not true to scale, it is clearly useless to measure with meticulous care the exact distances of these features from the sides of the surveyor's triangles. The approximate Representative Fraction of the plan of our field was $\frac{1}{2,000}$. The degree of fineness for a carefully drawn pencil line is at most about $\frac{1}{100}$ of an inch, and with an R.F. of $\frac{1}{2,000}$ this represents 20 inches on the ground. In addition to this, it is very unlikely that the most careful draughtsman will manage to draw his lines on the paper in their exactly true positions with an accuracy greater than another $\frac{1}{100}$ of an inch, so that 40 inches on the ground represents the error possible without affecting normal accuracy of the plan, while errors twice as large will not seriously affect it. Because of this, a great deal of time and labour can be saved in surveying by using quick methods of measuring. Many of the offsets in our field survey could have been measured by eye quite accurately enough for our purpose. Indeed, the practised surveyor knows so well the length of his walking pace that for ordinary purposes he can dispense with careful chaining, and measure by pacing with no greater error than some 2 per cent. Measurement of distance for purposes of map-making in previously unexplored territory is often done by calculating how far the horse, camel, canoe, or native porter can proceed in a given time, and then recording how long movement from point to point actually does take.

A word of warning must, however, be given. Approximate methods will not do when mathematical calculations or constructions are to be made from the resultant figures. For instance, when the apex of a triangle has to be plotted by intersecting arcs drawn about the ends of the triangle's base, the sides of the triangle must be measured with great care, unless check lines (such as CX and DY in our field) are also measured.

Calculation of Area. For the purpose of this book it is not necessary to go deeply into the manner in which the area of mapped territory is calculated. It is sufficient to say that by division of the ground into rectangles and triangles, the dimensions of which can easily be measured and the areas calculated, and then adding the figures together, the area of a territory as a whole can be found.

The formulæ for the calculation of the area of a triangle, given certain of the dimensions, are as follows

1. Area of Triangle $= \dfrac{\text{Perpendicular Height} \times \text{Base}}{2}$.

2. Area of Triangle $= \sqrt{s(s-a)\ (s-b)\ (s-c)}$
    where s is half the sum of the sides of the triangle, and a, b and c are the lengths of the respective sides.

CHAPTER TWO

DIRECTION

IT is usual to draw maps with the North at the top, so that South is at the bottom, and East and West are to the right and left respectively. There must be no taking it for granted, however, that the top of all maps is towards the North. Plans of towns, villages, and country areas are not as uniform as altas maps in this respect, and reference should always be made, when reading a map or plan, to the direction indicator drawn upon it, which gives true North. This is the direction of the North Pole, and the direction that the shadow of a stick will take on horizontal ground if held vertical at noon. Except for a negligible variation, it is also the direction of the Pole Star.

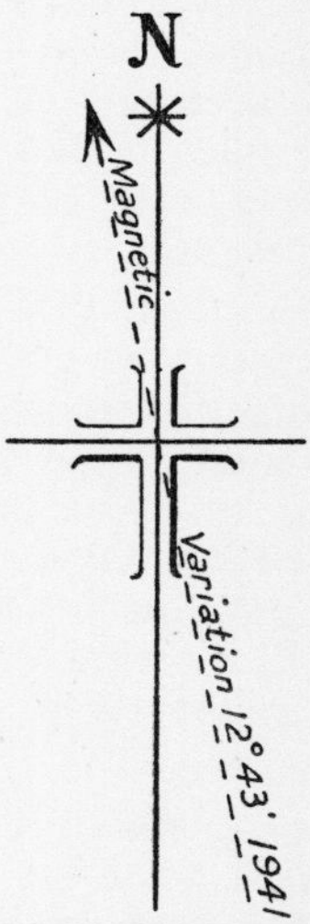

The typical direction indicator drawn in Fig. 8 shows North, South, East, and West by the four arms of a cross. To the west of North there is an arrow-head pointing at an angle away from the direction marked N. This is the direction that a magnetic compass will indicate. It is called the Magnetic North, and the angle it makes with true North, called the Magnetic variation, varies with time and place.

Magnetic Variation. In England, in 1941, the magnetic variation was 12° 43′ W., and it decreases at a rate which is not constant, but which is now about 7 minutes a year. Eventually the two Norths will coincide, and then magnetic North will swing past true North and appear to the east of it. The magnetic variation must always be taken into consideration when the compass is used to determine direction, both in map-making and map-reading.

FIG. 8.—A typical direction indicator.

Measuring Direction. In order to measure direction, the circle from North, right around the " clock ", and back again to North, is divided into 360 degrees ; each degree is subdivided into 60 minutes, and each minute into 60 seconds.

90° make a right angle, which is the difference of direction between North and East, East and South, etc., whilst 180° make a straight angle, the difference between North and South or between East and West.

Bearing. The measurement of the direction of a distant object from an observer is stated in terms of degrees, minutes, and seconds, and indicates the angle between North and the

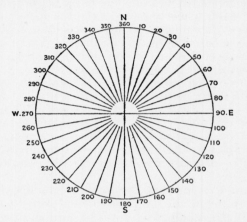

FIG. 9.—The division of the compass into degrees.

object, measured from North in a clockwise direction. This angle is called its bearing. For instance, if a church spire were observed due West, its bearing would be 270°. It is never necessary to quote a direction as so many degrees " East of North " or " clockwise from North ".

Remember, however, that the direction indicated by a magnetic compass is the Magnetic Bearing, whilst the direction from true North is the True Bearing. The two will differ by the magnetic variation, and must not be confused.

Back Bearing. The Back Bearing of a distant object is the bearing that the observer's position would have if it were measured by another person situated at the distant object. Always the back bearing of an object differs from its bearing by 180°. For instance, if the bearing of a church spire were 270°, it would be due West, but a person at the top of the spire would see the observer due East, or at a bearing of 90°. Then 90° is the back bearing of the spire.

Magnetic, True and Back Bearings must be thoroughly understood, for much in surveying and map-making, as well as in map-reading, depends upon them.

The Magnetic Compass. Mankind owes more to the Magnetic Compass than it realises, for navigation both of the sea and air has depended upon it since ships began to venture out of sight of land, whilst the exploration of new lands and the development of commerce routes across them have in similar manner been based upon the compass. Yet it is a simple instrument, even in one of its most highly developed and accurate forms, the prismatic compass.

The Simple Compass consists of a magnetised needle, suspended with free movement upon a pivot situated at the centre of a circle upon which are marked the points of the compass in 10° or 1° divisions. These parts are contained in a circular box with a glass lid, and if there are no magnetic influences, such as those of iron railings or pipes, to counteract the effect of the earth's magnetic axis, the needle will point to magnetic North.

The Card Compass has the circular graduated card suspended with the needle on the pivot, and is free to move with it. Usually the needle is beneath the card and invisible, but, as in the case of the simple compass, it is enclosed in a box with a glass lid.

In order to take a bearing of a distant object with either of the above types of magnetic compass, it is necessary to hold it steady until the needle comes to rest. The simple compass is then turned till North on the card lies immediately under the point of the needle ; in the case of the card compass the card has turned with the needle, and has already taken its correct position. A line is then imagined between the centre of the compass and the distant object, and its angle from North read upon the card. This is the bearing, but it is evident that accuracy is difficult when the line across the centre of the compass to the distant object can only be imagined.

The Prismatic Compass, illustrated in Fig. 10, is an accurate instrument of the card-compass type, the card upon which degrees are marked moving with the needle. The correct line of sight to a distant object need not be imagined in this case.

The observer holds the compass close to one eye and looks
through a slit in a little window fixed to the rim of the compass, and gets the distant object in alignment with a vertical
hair-line drawn across the glass lid of the compass box opened
up vertically on the opposite side of the rim.   Behind the
window-slit is a prism which saves the observer having to
turn his eyes down to the card to read the bearing.   While
looking at the distant object he sees at the same time the
required figure.

FIG. 10.—Prismatic Compass.

It will be noticed that the prism is above the point of the
card opposite to, or 180° away from, the point where on an
ordinary card compass the correct bearing figure would
appear.   Because of this, the prismatic-compass card has
two markings ·of degrees : an inner one with graduations
marked exactly the same as in an ordinary compass, and an
outer one with graduations differing by 180°.   The reading
brought so conveniently before the observer's eye by the
prism is from the outer ring, and is thus the correct bearing.

The prism also magnifies the figures, and its effect is to
reflect in reverse, as a mirror does, so that the figures are
printed on the card in reverse, to be shown to the observer

the right way round. There is an adjusting screw, so that the magnified figures can be focused to suit the eye.

The Protractor is a drawing instrument consisting either of a rectangular piece of box-wood or a semi-circular piece of celluloid. At the centre of the bottom edge of the first type and of the straight edge of the semi-circular type is a point at which a line is drawn across the instrument at right angles or 90°. Along the opposite edge are marked the degree graduations, each with two sets of figures, 0° to 180° and 180° to 360°. Each is used to plot bearings and back bearings on the plan or map when map-making, or to take them from the map when map-reading.

To plot a bearing on a map, the protractor is laid with its bottom edge along the magnetic or true North–South line, according to whether the bearing is the magnetic or true one, with the centre point at the position of the observer. The point on the map on the other side of the protractor where the bearing figure appears is marked, the instrument removed, and the observer's position joined to the point with a line. This line gives the correct bearing for the object observed.

The Theodolite is a very accurate and expensive instrument used only in the most precise surveying. It is not necessary to explain its design and use in this book, because such detail will not help in the appreciation of how maps are made. For our purpose it is sufficient to say that it consists of telescopic sights and graduated scales, so that by aligning one sight on to one distant object, and another sight on a second distant object, the exact angle between them can be read to an accuracy of one second (1″). The instrument can also be used to measure the angle of a distant object above or below the horizontal, the purpose of which is explained in Chapter III.

The Traverse. The reader has now the necessary knowledge to follow the surveyor in the mapping of geographical features such as rivers, roads, tracks through unexplored country, coastlines, and the boundaries of fields, parishes, or any other kind of area.

The method is known as the traverse, and consists of following the line of the road or other feature, measuring its direction and length while it remains straight, measuring the angle of its turn and the next straight length, and continuing until the end of the feature is reached. If the course of the line is sinuous in places, the degree of curve from the general straight-line direction is measured by offsets. All figures obtained are recorded in the field note-book in the methodical manner already described, the bearing of each new direction being placed in a special column on the extreme left of the note-book page.

The traverse can be carried out by precise methods, using the theodolite and steel measuring tape, or by the more usual method with chain and prismatic compass. A high level of accuracy can be obtained by carefully pacing distances, or by using a wheeled device for measurement that records revolutions over the ground, these revolutions being converted into linear units.

Large traverses in new countries are often carried out with the compass to measure direction, and the time taken at a known rate of movement by horse, camel, or native porter to measure distance. One of the authors, making surveys in Africa, carried out a traverse along a winding stream surrounded by marsh which could only be approached by a canoe. He counted the number of paddle-strokes along a measured bank, and found that each stroke of the paddlers sent the canoe along $4\frac{1}{2}$ feet. He then counted the number of paddle-strokes made in a given time, so that when passing over long distances he would know, from the total time taken, the approximate number of paddle-strokes, each taking the canoe along $4\frac{1}{2}$ feet, that had been made from start to finish.

At the end of a 27-mile traverse, during which he detailed a small boy to beat a gong to keep the paddling uniform, he found that the error was less than 3 per cent.

A *Closed Traverse* is one in which the starting point is also the finishing point, for the route traversed eventually returns to where it began. Such would be the case when traversing the boundary of a field, or along one road and back along one or more others.

An *Open Traverse* is one in which the starting point and the finishing point are not the same, such as in the case of a path or track across country.

The closed traverse is self-checking, for when the map is plotted from the Field Book, progress along the line according to the recorded figures should make the starting and finishing

oints coincide. If they fail to do so, the distance between
them is called the *Error of Closure*.

The open traverse is not self-checking, and should be
checked by one of three methods :—

1. The bearing and distance of the finishing point
from the starting point should be measured, by protractor and scale, on the Ordnance Map, or whatever is
the best available map of the area. The correct position
of the finishing point should then be plotted on the plan,
and the distance between the true position and that
arrived at by the traverse is the error of closure.

2. Whilst the traverse is being made in the field, the
bearing of some prominent landmark should be taken
at the end of each straight length of the route before the
turn is made to the next leg. If the landmark is not
always visible, bearings should be taken from those
stations from which it can be seen. When the traverse
is plotted on the map, these bearings are drawn as rays
in pencil, and if the work has been done correctly, they
will intersect at one point only—the true relative position
of the landmark.

3. The most direct route back to the starting point
should be traversed. This amounts to closing the
originally open traverse and providing a new finishing
point that should coincide with the starting point when
plotted on the map.

Adjustment of the Error of Closure. It is difficult to perform
large surveys without some amount of error. The error of
closure discovered when a traverse is plotted is not so serious
a matter as to make it necessary to begin the traverse all over
again and check the measurements until the error is reduced
to zero. This would be necessary only if the error were
sufficiently large to make the plotted map seriously incorrect.
On the other hand, some way must be found to bring the
finishing point of a traverse to its correct position. It cannot
be left where the plotted traverse takes it, if that position is
known to be wrong.

Expecting some degree of error, the draughtsman makes a
trial drawing of the traverse legs to discover the amount of

the Error of Closure. Suppose that in Fig. 11, *ABCD* is the
quadrilateral shape of a traversed boundary to a field. The
last side from *D* fails to meet *A* when the trial drawing is
made, so let us suppose this side finishes at A_1. Then A_1 to
A is the error of closure. Evidently errors have been made
during the traverse, the total net amount of which is equal to
the length of A_1A. Clearly it would be wrong to close the
quadrilateral by arbitrarily drawing *D* to *A* and apportioning
all the necessary adjustment of length and direction to the one
line *DA*. The length A_1A and the change of direction needed

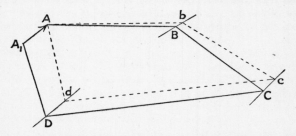

FIG. 11.—Adjustment of the error of closure in a closed traverse.

to close the quadrilateral must be apportioned between the
various legs of the traverse, for there is likely to be part of the
total error in each. The chances of error increase with distance,
so that it would be best to apportion the error according
to distance.

This the draughtsman does by drawing a line on the paper
the total length of the traverse and dividing it into the individual lengths of the legs, *AB*, *BC*, *CD*, *DA* (see Fig. 12). If
the length of $ABCDA_1$ is too long for the paper, the whole
line can be reduced in scale, as long as the traverse legs are
shown in correct proportion. At the end of the line a perpendicular is erected of the full length of the error of closure A_1A.
It is not reduced in scale as the base line may have been. A
third line is drawn joining the beginning of the first line to the
top of the perpendicular, to make the hypoteneuse of the
triangle AAA_1, and other perpendiculars are erected at *B*, *C*
and *D*, of a height so that they meet the hypoteneuse. The
lengths of the perpendiculars *B*, *C*, *D*, and A_1 are then the

correct distances for the respective corners of the quadrilateral to be moved in order to close the traverse. The figure constructed and shown in Fig. 12 is called the Error Scale.

Now, A_1 (in Fig. 11) has to be moved in the direction of A, so parallels to this direction through B, C, and D will give the direction for their movement. These parallels are drawn, and distances marked off with dividers equal to the lengths of the perpendiculars Bb, Cc, Dd. The quadrilateral $Abcd$ will then be the new position for the traverse, with each leg bearing a degree of adjustment proportional to its length.

If the traverse had been an open one instead of closed, the error of closure revealed on a trial map by one of the methods of checking is apportioned between the various legs in the

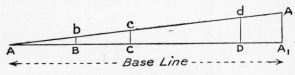

FIG. 12.—The Error Scale.

same way. Parallels to the direction of the error of closure through the points where the traverse alters direction are drawn, and along these the distances determined by the error scale are marked, just as in the case of the closed traverse.

Intersection. In Chapter I we learned how it was possible to plot the position of one corner of a triangle when the lengths of each side had been measured. We did this with intersecting arcs drawn about the ends of the already plotted base line.

In this present chapter we have learned, in addition, how, in traversing, the point at the end of each leg is plotted after the compass bearing of the line and its length have been measured. It will now be necessary to learn the method of plotting the position of a distant object when it is inconvenient or impossible to measure its distance away. This is done by taking bearings of the unknown position of the object from two known positions. Let us suppose that we have already mapped by the traverse method two roads ACB and $ADEB$, and that between them is a boggy tract of country across which it is dangerous to pass and certainly impossible

to chain distances. Suppose that Q is the position of a rocky
crag on an island of firm ground, and we wish to plot it
position on the map. By use of the prismatic compass we find
that its bearing from A is 95° and from D the bearing is 60°
The protractor is put on the paper with its bottom edge along
the vertical magnetic north–south line, and the centre point
at A. 95° are measured off along the graduated edge and
marked with a dot X. The protractor is removed and the
thin line AX drawn in. Similarly a line DY is drawn with
a bearing of 60° from D, and DY cuts AX at Q. Then the
point of intersection gives the position of the rocky crag.

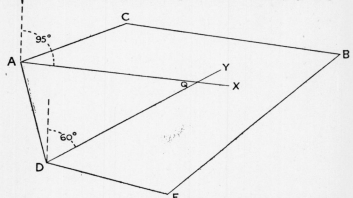

FIG. 13.—Plotting a point by intersection from two known positions.

In survey work covering a large area it is sometimes necessary to use intersection as the principal method of determining the framework of the map into which detail is late.
to be put. Perhaps a previously unsurveyed tract of territory
has to be mapped, and the nature of the country and absence
of boundary lines make traversing inconvenient. In this case
a beginning will be made by carefully measuring a straight
line between two stations and using it as a base line, from the
ends of which the bearings of distant objects can be taken and
their relative positions determined. Once the position of these
objects is known, they in turn can be used to enlarge the field
of survey and to discover the relative positions of more distan
objects.

This method of mapping an area is called Triangulation, and will be described at greater length in Chapter IV.

Before we leave the subject of intersection, however, it is necessary to mention that the possibility of error in taking bearings has to be taken into consideration. It would be clearly unwise to proceed with the survey of a large area by triangulation unless a negligible amount of error could be assumed for the position of each point used as a survey station, these themselves having been plotted by intersection.

For this reason two lines of intersection are never considered sufficient to give accuracy. For instance, if it were essential

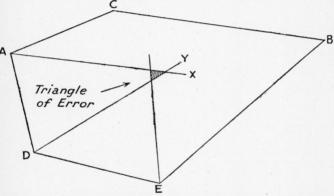

Fig. 14.—The triangle of error caused by errors made in the taking of bearings.

that the position determined for our rocky crag should be accurate, a third bearing would be taken from another known point, such as E, and a third intersecting line drawn. If the latter passed through the point Q exactly, the surveyor would congratulate himself, and give Q the status of first-class accuracy.

If, however, any mistakes had been made in the three bearings taken, the third line would not pass through Q, and would cause a small triangle to be formed, as in Fig. 14. The size of this triangle relative to the distances under consideration would indicate the extent of the mistakes, and if it were large, a fourth bearing would be taken from another known

position. If the triangle were minute, the surveyor would
probably give it the status of first-class accuracy and use the
station as one for triangulation.   Small triangles would give
an indication of only second-class accuracy, not to be relied
upon for further triangulation ;   and larger triangles indicate
positions of poor accuracy not on any account to be used as
stations for further survey.

Resection.   Just as it is possible to determine the unknown
position of a distant object by taking bearings from two or
more known positions, so it is possible to plot on a map one's

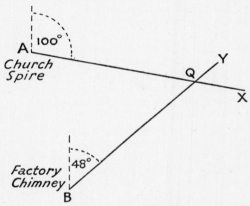

Fig. 15.—Plotting a point by resection from two known positions.

own position by taking back bearings of two or more distant
objects.   This is called Resection.

Let us suppose that it is necessary to find one's position in
open country, and back bearings of a church spire *A*, and
factory chimney *B*, are found to be 100° and 48° respectively.
Then the protractor will be laid on the map with the centre
point at *A*, and the bottom edge on the magnetic North–South
line.   100° are marked off along the edge, and the line *AX* is
drawn.   Similarly the line *BY* is drawn with a direction of
48° from *B*.   If *Q* is the point of intersection, it will be the
observer's position.

In the paragraphs about intersection it was stated that
three-line intersection is required to confirm accuracy, before

the position determined can be used as a station for extending the survey. The same conditions apply to points fixed by resection.

Sketching in Detail. Detail in a map is often drawn by eye during the process of a survey. To do this it is necessary to determine the observer's position relative to already plotted topographical features, by resection, and to " set " the map on the ground or tripod table so that the North point of the map points to the north of the country. Once that is done it is possible to see the correct position and direction on the map of all features seen in the vicinity of the observer's position, and they can be sketched in.

The following are the methods by which a map can be set, and it should be noticed that to have the features of a map in the correct position relative to the actual lie of the land is of use to the map-reader as well as to the map-maker. Very often does the rambler, the cyclist, or the motorist set his map, to make easier the checking or the choosing of his route, or to identify something seen in the distance.

1. *Setting by Compass.* Both the magnetic and true North directions will be indicated on the sheet before the map is drawn. If a compass be placed upon the direction indicator, and the map turned until the line of magnetic North is in alignment with the compass needle, the map will be set.

2. *Setting by Already Plotted Positions.* A straight-edge is placed upon the map so that it lies along the straight line joining the observer's position to that of a distant object which can be recognised in the country, such as a church spire. The map is turned until the straight-edge points directly to the object.

3. *Setting by the Sun.* True North can be found by holding a watch horizontally and turning it so that the line bisecting the angle between 12 o'clock and the hour-hand points directly to the sun. If the watch shows correct Greenwich Mean Time (not B.S.T.), 12 o'clock will now point due South and six o'clock due North. If the watch lies upon the map, the latter can then be turned beneath the watch until its true North direction is in alignment with the 6 o'clock–12 o'clock line of the watch.

4. *Setting by Straight Roads, Railways, etc.* A map can be set by turning it until the direction of a straight length of

road, railway or canal upon the map is parallel to the straight length it represents in the field.

When sketching on a map the details seen in the field near the observer, the relative distances are measured by chain or pacing, and converted to scale units.

To take an example, we will suppose the surveyor has set his map by compass at the junction of four paths, and that around him are meadows in which there are a pond, a barn, a stream, and a mill. By drawing rays from his own plotted position in the direction of these features, or to some distinct point on them, such as the turn of a path or a bridge over the stream, he gets their direction right. By chaining or pacing he finds their distances from his own plotted position, and by converting these to scale units he finds the correct distance to mark off along the appropriate rays, and can sketch them in to their true scale size. By this means a considerable portion of the map can be sketched at each resected station.

CHAPTER THREE

HEIGHT

DISTANCE, area, and direction are not the only characteristics of geographical features that are represented on a map or plan. Methods of measuring and indicating the height above sea-level and the shapes of hill or mountain country involve problems which the map-maker has to solve.

There are various methods of showing the height of hill features, and it is best to know the nature of each.

Spot Heights. It is a common practice to indicate the height above sea-level of hill-tops and mountain peaks by small figures. This is a useful method used together with a second one, but by themselves the spot heights do not convey a mental picture of the shapes of hills, the gradient of slopes or the direction of spurs and valleys.

Contours. Except when drawn on a very small scale, English maps have lines drawn through points of equal height, which are called contour lines. From one contour to the next there is a rise or fall of a certain amount, known as the Vertical Interval, and usually this is the same between each contour line, but reference should be made to the marginal information of a map before assuming this. Often the height represented by each contour is entered in small figures upon it, or upon every other one, or every third one ; whilst the height of the top of the hill or mountain is indicated by spot-height figures. To be accurate, contours should be surveyed as carefully as geographical features like roads, rivers, or boundaries, and, as described later, this requires a great deal of surveying in the field.

Form Lines are unsurveyed contours, drawn in by eye to show the formation of the ground in hills, valleys, spurs, etc. When contours are used with a big vertical interval, form lines are often interpolated between them to indicate alterations in height that the contours are too far apart to show. They have a great value where it is necessary to save time and labour, but it should be noticed how limited in accuracy they are.

Hachures are short lines showing the direction of slope— thick and close to one another for steep slopes, thin and wider apart for those that are less steep. Flat ground is left plain. They give a very good idea of the general formation of hill and mountain country, but do not show the exact heights, as do contours. Spot-height figures at frequent intervals are necessary to make up for this, and the method is not now used much in this country, except with contours.

Hill-Shading. There are two distinct methods of representing hilly country by this system. Neither shows absolute heights, only the general hill formation.

The first shows the mapped area as it would appear if illuminated from directly above with a bright light. Hill-tops and flat country are left unshaded, slight slopes are lightly shaded, while steep slopes are represented by a darker tone.

The second method imagines the source of light to be north-west of the mapped area, so that eastern and southern slopes are shaded, the degree of slope being indicated by the depth of tone. This method is used on British Ordnance Survey 1-inch Relief Maps.

Contours and Hachures are used together on the 1-inch Ordnance Survey Relief Maps. The contours are the more important feature, the hachures being used to indicate minor hill formations when the vertical interval between the contours is too large for them to be used.

Contours and Hill-Shading. This is another method in which contours are used to show the major alterations in height, while the hill-shading is included to make the map more readable at a glance.

Contours and Layer Tints. In this method it is usual to colour green all land lying between sea-level and the 100-foot contour line. A lighter green is used to colour the space between the 100-foot contour and the next, and shades of brown varying in intensity according to the height are used between the others.

The great advantage of this system is that the distribution of high and low ground can be seen at a glance, but owing to the limited number of shades of brown available for map-printing, it is often necessary to use one shade for more than one vertical interval. This demands careful reference to the marginal information before all ground coloured the same shade can be assumed to lie between the limits of two contours.

Although contour lines are not generally used by themselves, it is plain that they form the basis of the usual methods of representing height.

Three methods of determining height will be examined in the light of contour drawing. They are as follows :

1. By *clinometer*, an instrument which measures the angle of slope to the horizontal, made by a straight line from the observer up or down hill to a distant object.

2. By *levelling*, when the difference in height between two points on a slope is measured directly. Alternatively, the level is used to find the position of points of equal height, which are marked with sticks or surveyor's staffs. The correct position on the map for the imaginary line which joins these marked points is then found by a traverse.

3. By *Surveyor's Aneroid Barometer*, an instrument which makes use of the fact that atmospheric pressure decreases with height. A needle moving over a graduated scale records the increase or decrease in height as the user moves from one point on a hill to another.

In all considerations of height it is the mean sea-level that is taken as zero (see page 124). When England was mapped by the Ordnance Survey, the accurate height of many key positions about the country was measured and marked on stone or wooden posts, or on buildings, near ground-level. These marks, indicated by a broad arrow below a horizontal line, are called Bench-marks, and their exact height is also indicated on the 6-inch Ordnance Plans. Whenever surveying of heights is now carried out, these bench-marks can be used to determine the height of the stations from which the work proceeds.

The Clinometer and its Use. This instrument measures the vertical angle of an object above or below the horizontal, and there are many patterns, all using the same principle.

A spirit-level, or a plumb-line and weight, provides the means by which the clinometer is kept in its correct position. The sights, which are usually telescopic, are focused upon the distant object, and the angle reading is shown on an attached scale of degrees.

Before beginning his work the surveyor decides the difference in height which will be represented by the space between two contours. As already mentioned, this is the Vertical Interval, or V.I. It is evident that to represent a slope which remains the same for a given distance, contours will be an equal interval apart, since the distance required for the ground to rise or fall a number of feet equal to the vertical interval is the same as long as the angle of slope remains constant.

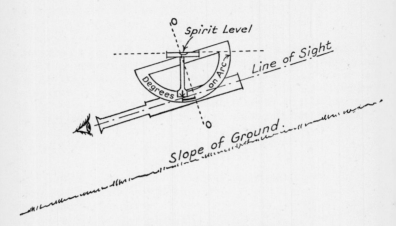

FIG. 16.—The principle of the clinometer.

If the slope were steeper, the contours would be closer together, and if slighter, the contours would be farther apart.

By means of mathematical calculation the surveyor provides himself with a table which tells him how far apart to

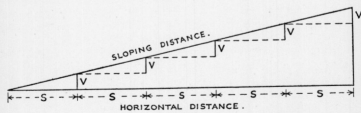

V = *Vertical Interval.*   S = *Space between contours.*

FIG. 17.—For a constant angle of slope and a constant vertical interval the contours are the same distance apart.

draw contours for a given V.I. at 1° of slope, 2°, 3°, and so on for all slopes he is likely to meet in the course of his survey. The mathematical calculation is as follows :

FIG. 18.

Suppose that in the triangle ABC, CA is the sloping distance represented on a map between two contours, CB is the horizontal distance between them, and AB is the Vertical Interval. Since AB is vertical and CB horizontal the triangle ABC is right-angled.

Suppose that the angle of slope, angle ACB, is θ.

$$\text{Now, } \frac{AB}{BC} = \text{Tangent } ACB = \text{Tangent } \theta$$

$$\text{Therefore } BC = \frac{AB}{\text{Tangent } \theta}$$

$$\text{That is, Horizontal Distance} = \frac{\text{Vertical Interval}}{\text{Tangent of Angle of Slope}}.$$

By reference to Tangent Tables,

$$\text{Tangent } 1° = \cdot 0175 = \frac{1}{57 \cdot 3} = \frac{1}{60} \text{ nearly.}$$

and similarly

Tangent 2° = 1/30 nearly.
Tangent 3° = 1/20 nearly.
Tangent 4° = 1/15 nearly.
Tangent 5° = 1/12 nearly.
Tangent 6° = 1/10 nearly.

By using these figures the Horizontal Distance can be calculated from the formula :

$$\text{H.D.} = \frac{\text{V.I.}}{\text{Tan. Angle of slope}},$$

for varying degrees of slope, and a table constructed.

Table for Horizontal Distance between Contours.

For 1° of slope H.D. = V.I. × 60
    2°   H.D. = V.I. × 30
    3°   H.D. = V.I. × 20
    4°   H.D. = V.I. × 15
    5°   H.D. = V.I. × 12
    6°   H.D. = V.I. × 10

The table can be continued for all degrees of slope likely to be met with in ordinary survey work, but the approximate value of the tangent as used above would not give sufficient accuracy for larger angles than 12°.

Once the surveyor has decided upon his vertical interval, he applies the actual figure to the above table, and this gives him the distance in feet which he must represent on the map between the contours, for the angle of slope of the particular piece of ground he is surveying.[1]

It must be remembered that the distance measured along the ground up or down a hill is the sloping distance, not the horizontal distance. This was explained on page 19. When the angle of slope is small compared with the sloping distance, the latter is very little different from its horizontal equivalent, and might be used for it in the above calculation. For accuracy, however, an adjustment must be made according to the table given on page 20.

The Actual Survey (see Fig. 19). When surveying a hill for the purpose of contour drawing, the first step is to decide upon a suitable position upon its summit for the station from which to begin. The height above sea-level of this point should be obtained either by reference to the Ordnance Survey plan, or by calculation, as explained in the note below, from the known height of a bench-mark. The V.I. is decided upon—say 20 feet—and the work begins by the use of the clinometer to

---

[1] The above table can also be used to find the height of one object above another, if the horizontal distance between them and the angle of slope is known.

Thus, if the H.D. is 600 feet and the angle of slope is 4°.

$$H.D. = V.I. × 15.$$

That is   600 feet = V.I. (or Height) × 15.

Therefore $V.I. = \dfrac{600}{15}$ feet = 40 feet.

measure the angle of slope downhill in a certain direction. This may be along the valley of a stream, or towards a church spire, or in a direction due North : it does not matter so long as the direction can be found easily upon the map to which contours are to be added as well as on the hill itself. Minor undulations of the ground are ignored, and only the general angle of slope is measured, so far as it remains constant.

Where it is seen that the general angle of slope changes, a staff will be placed, to mark the position of the next station from which a reading will be taken. The clinometer should be held at eye-level, and sighted upon a mark upon the staff also at eye-level, or held close to the ground and sighted on the staff at a point upon it also near the ground.

In the following example it will be best, for the sake of clearness, if no adjustment is made to convert sloping distance to horizontal equivalent. We will use deliberately the distance chained along the ground as the distance indicated on the map, though to do this is not strictly accurate.

Let the angle of slope be 4°, the distance between the stations arrived at by chaining 300 yards, and the height of the first station 215 feet. Applying the vertical interval of 20 feet to the table on page 42, we see that the horizontal distance between contours will be, for 4°, 20 feet × 15, or 100 yards. Contours drawn between the first station and the second will be this distance apart.

A line is drawn on the map from the position of the first station, in the direction chosen—say due North—and according to the scale of the map, a mark is made representing the second station 300 yards away. By our calculation a fall of 20 feet occurs in each 100 yards. But the first station is 215 feet above sea-level, and we wish our first contour to show a height of 200 feet. Therefore, by simple proportion, we calculate that a fall of the first 15 feet will take place in 75 yards. So the position for the 200-foot contour is marked a distance representing 75 yards along the line. The position of each successive contour until the second station is reached will be 100 yards beyond the previous one. The last contour before the change of slope at No. 2 Station will be 275 yards from the first station. No. 2 Station will thus be 25 yards beyond the last contour.

As there is a drop of 20 feet in each 100 yards, there is one of 5 feet in 25 yards, and so Station No. 2 is 5 feet below the last contour.

Let the angle of slope measured downhill with the clinometer from Station No. 2 be 2°, and the distance to the next

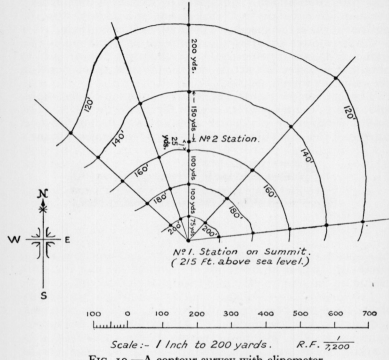

FIG. 19.—A contour survey with clinometer.

change of slope, Station No. 3, 1,000 yards. Our table tells us that the new distance between contours must be 20 feet (the V.I.) × 30, which is 200 yards. Station No. 2 was 5 feet below the last contour and, the V.I. being 20 feet, it must be 15 feet above the next.

A 20-foot fall for 200 yards means a 15-foot fall for 150 yards, so that the first contour after No. 2 Station will be that scale distance below it. This is marked along the line.

Successive points will be plotted till No. 3 Station is reached, and the procedure continued for as far as the survey makes it necessary.

The operation is repeated in directions all round the compass from Station No. 1, until a series of lines is obtained on the map, all radiating from that station and marked with the positions where the successive contours will cross them. It is a simple matter to draw the complete contours upon this framework, regard being paid to the help the eye can give to obtain their direction across the unsurveyed space between the radiating direction-lines.

The clinometer method of fixing contours is very rapid, and does not entail a great deal of labour in the field. The results obtained have a degree of accuracy sufficient for most purposes, but it should be noticed that it is the general angle

Fig. 20.—Pocket sighting-level.

of slope in a limited number of straight-line directions that is surveyed. Minor undulations are ignored because the work would be too lengthy if account were taken of them.

Levelling. The Ordnance Survey, to whom we are indebted for our best maps of England, used the extremely tedious but precise method of determining the position of contours on the ground by means of the surveyor's level, marking them with pegs, and traversing the lines joining them.

There are various types of level, but the principle is the same in each. The ordinary pocket instrument consists of a hollow tube about $4\frac{1}{2}$ inches long, fitted with peep-sights, which may be telescopic. A spirit-level is attached, and when the level is sighted upon a distant object, the spirit-bubble is reflected by a small mirror, so that the horizontal position can be maintained. A weighted string exactly 5 feet long is usually attached to the level so that its height above the ground when in use is constant. When used to determine the position of contours on the ground in the precise manner of the Ordnance Survey, the surveyor begins at a spot of already calculated height, and sights the instrument upon the sloping ground in front of him. He indicates to assistants the position of a number of points level with his instrument, which is, of course, 5 feet above the ground he stands on. These points are marked by pegs, and show the line of the contour. Then he advances to one of the pegs and repeats the process, so that a new contour is pegged above the first. The pegging of a whole hill is not particularly difficult, but the subsequent traversing of each of the contour lines he intends to represent on his map takes a great deal of the surveyor's time and trouble.

Another method which is quicker and less troublesome, but also less precise, is to proceed uphill towards the summit from the first station (of previously calculated height), with an assistant walking on ahead. When he has advanced so far that his feet are level with the instrument held by the surveyor, it is known that the point upon which he stands is five feet above the first station. The pair move on, the second position becoming a second station, until the height of points all the way from the bottom to the top is known. The distance between the successive stations is chained or paced, and recorded with the heights in the Field Book. It will then be necessary to proceed along another direction to the summit of the hill, and similarly record the height and distance figures. From the Field Book the contours can then be drawn on the map in the surveyor's office.

It will be noticed that the chained distance is the sloping distance. It is the horizontal equivalent of this which should be used to space the contours upon the map. If distance is great compared with the angle of slope, the difference might be ignored, but in accurate work the figure would be adjusted, as explained on page 19.

The Use of the Surveyor's Aneroid Barometer. The ordinary barometer is an instrument which measures the weight of the atmosphere above it, and as atmospheric pressure decreases with height to the extent of 1 inch to 900 feet, the surveyor makes use of the instrument to compare heights. For this purpose there is a special adaptation of the aneroid barometer, fitted with a height scale in feet in addition to the atmospheric pressure scale in inches. In the absence of disturbing influences, the watch or pocket instrument, of about 3 inches in diameter, will give a reading accurate to 5 feet.

Unfortunately there are other influences affecting baro-metric pressure besides height. The weight of air varies with its density, which in turn varies with temperature, so that a thermometer must be used in conjunction with the aneroid. In addition, it is possible for barometric pressure to alter while the survey is in progress, so that a key barometer should be kept at the first station, and variations of pressure recorded with their times, so that read-ings taken at other stations can be adjusted.

Because of these influences, the accuracy of the aneroid method of determining differ-ences of height is limited, and it is used for the survey of new countries and other pre-viously unexplored areas, rather than for exact surveys such as have been described, where the clinometer or level gives better results.

Fig. 21.—Pocket aneroid barometer.

It should be realised that in all surveying of heights it will be wise to provide checks as the work proceeds. For instance, it has been explained how the absolute height of the No. 1 Station of the clinometer survey was obtained, by reference to a bench-mark. If the survey is extended to include the position of the bench-mark, its height above sea-level as calculated from the survey from the No. 1 Station should be compared with its actual height as indicated upon it. The two should, of course, be the same, but if they are not, a proportional adjustment of the successive contours should be made.

CHAPTER FOUR

MAPPING LARGE TRACTS OF COUNTRY

In Chapter I, when examining the surveyor's methods of planning an irregularly shaped field, we saw that division of the total area into triangles was essential for constructing the framework about which the ultimate plan was drawn. From records kept in the Field Book the draughtsman found it possible to plot first the correctly shaped triangles, and then the detail of boundaries, paths and buildings.

Countries are also surveyed by division of their territory into triangles, but the shape and size of these triangles are determined, not by chaining the sides, but by measurement of angles taken from each end of a measured base line to the apex. If in any triangle the length of the base and the angles at the base are known, the length of the other sides can be calculated, or the position of the apex can be plotted immediately upon the map.

This method of surveying is called Triangulation, and its usefulness in map-making will now be shown by explaining how a hitherto unsurveyed island of considerable size can be accurately represented to scale on paper.

The first necessity is to explore the island, to become familiar with its general shape and size, and to decide upon the best way of dividing the island into triangles. When surveying the irregular field, the corners of each triangle were marked by surveyor's staffs ; on the island, where distances are much greater, it is necessary to indicate the positions of Trigonometrical Stations, as the points are called, by building cairns of stones, or erecting pyramid shapes. On many hills in England are seen the cairns and shapes constructed when the Ordnance Survey made their triangulations.

Next, a convenient site for a base line is chosen, where the ground is flat and can easily be measured as accurately as the survey requires. For the survey of England an 8-mile base line on Salisbury Plain was used, and to measure it with sufficient accuracy took six months. Steel tapes or wires are used, and allowances have to be made for temperature. If there is any slope in the ground, a calculation must be made to discover the exact horizontal distance between the ends.

Depending upon the importance of the survey, a base line will be measured on the island more or less accurately, and for a large area, some 50 miles from end to end, it should be at least 1 mile long. Before one attempts to determine the position

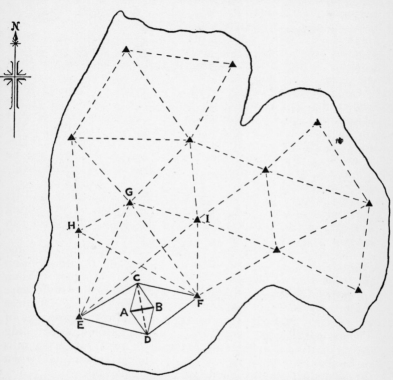

FIG. 22.—The triangulation of a hitherto unsurveyed island.

of the nearer trigonometrical stations, the base should be extended by means of well-conditioned triangles on each side of it. In Fig. 22, the base line is represented by the thick line *AB*. *C* and *D* are points distant from the base line, and plainly marked so that their relative positions can be determined by intersection from *A* and *B*. The theodolite will be

D

used if great accuracy is essential, as in work by the Ordnance Survey, but the prismatic compass is the instrument likely to be used in previously unexplored countries.

CD will be used as a base to find the positions of distant points *E* and *F*, by intersection, and *EF* will be the base from which the great work of triangulation will begin. Trigonometrical stations will be erected at each end.

The positions *G*, *H*, and *I* are determined by intersection from *E* and *F*. *HG*, *GI*, and *IF* are each in turn used as base lines to determine the position of more distant stations, and the work proceeds in this way, from one base line to another, till the whole island is covered with a network of triangles.

The accuracy of this work is checked by measuring accurately a second base line on the far side of the island, and comparing its measured length with that calculated by triangulation.

After this part of the survey is completed, it is necessary to divide the island into sections, in order to proceed with the detailed surveying. Several of the trigonometrical stations appear on each of the sheets representing the sections, and the details of topography, including hill features, are inserted by use of the methods we have already examined, or by plane tabling, which has yet to be described.

Methods Used for Insertion of Detail In and About the Triangulation Framework

Chain Surveying. This is the method described in Chapter I for mapping an irregularly shaped field. The area under consideration is mapped by division into well-conditioned triangles, the sides of which are short enough to be measured accurately with a Gunter's chain. Records of all necessary measurements are recorded in the field note-book for use by the draughtsman.

Intersection. The position of distant points is discovered by taking bearings from two or more known stations. The work extends as two or more points are plotted accurately enough for use as known stations. While visiting each position the map is set and detail in the neighbourhood sketched in.

Resection. The observer's position is found by taking back-bearings of two or more known stations, the work extending as more and more points are plotted accurately enough for use as known stations. Detail is sketched in after setting the map at each point.

Traversing, by which a road, river or boundary is mapped.

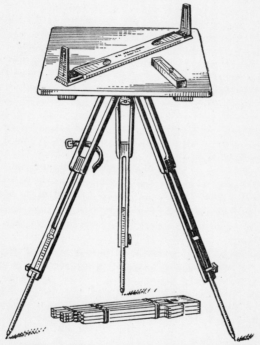

FIG. 23.—The plane table with its alidade and box compass.

Use of the Clinometer, Level, or Aneroid Barometer, by which the form of hill features is surveyed.

Plane Tabling, which is a method embodying the principles of Intersection and Resection.

The Plane Table consists of a well-made table-top varying in size from 15 inches square to about 18 inches by 24, which fits on to a folding tripod stand. It is easily portable, but very rigid when fixed and in use. The top can be revolved around its centre pivot, or screwed tightly so that no movement is possible. No magnetic metal is used in its construction.

Upon the table-top the sheet of paper on which the map is to be drawn is placed, the sides turned over the edge of the table and pasted on the underside, so that no movement of the paper is possible until the work is finished.

To make easier the setting of the table, a Box or Trough Compass is provided, consisting of a magnetic needle about 6 inches long, pivoted in the centre of a trough. This is housed in a rectangular wooden box, open at the top, carefully constructed with exactly parallel sides. The needle cannot revolve a full circle, because the box is too narrow, but short graduated arcs of 20° or so are placed at each end. The immediate purpose of the construction is to allow the box to be turned upon the plane table until the needle takes up the 0° position showing that the sides of the box are in a magnetic North–South direction.

The third item in the plane tabler's outfit is the Sighting Rule or Alidade, which in its simplest form is but a straight-edge, at the ends of which are sights. By looking through the backsight and aligning the foresight upon a distant object, the straight-edge gives the exact direction between the observer and the object.

Usually the alidade is made of box-wood and has bevelled edges, along which are graduated a number of useful scales for the plane-tabler's convenience. The sights are upright when in use, but are made to fold flat. In the backsight there is a narrow slit, and in the other a vertical wire or hair for use as a sighting vane.

The use of the plane table is twofold. First, when the framework of a survey is already plotted upon the sheet of paper on the table, it can be used to fill in the detail. We will see its use in this way by completing the map of the island already triangulated. Secondly, it can be used to plot both the detail and the framework of a survey, in which case the work begins from each end of a measured base line and extends as the positions of distant points are established.

Use of the Plane Table as Applied to Already Triangulated Territory.

On page 50 we saw that after triangulation it was necessary to divide the island into sections, each to be surveyed for detail separately. There will be a map-sheet for each section, and the first step is to plot the correct relative positions of all the trigonometrical stations coming within the section.

The table is taken to one of the stations and firmly fixed upon the ground. On it is placed the alidade, with its edge along the straight line joining the observer's position as plotted on the map with that of a second station. The table is then revolved about its pivot until the distant station is in alignment with the sighting vane. The table now being set, the screw is tightened to prevent further movement.

Next the box compass is placed upon the table and turned so that the needle comes to rest upon the o° line. Pencil lines are drawn on the map along each of the parallel box sides, so that the table can be set by compass at any subsequent position in the field.

If the trigonometrical stations coming within this section of the island have been plotted on the map correctly, it will now be possible to sight them one by one with the alidade placed with its edge along the corresponding line on the map.

It is clear that detail in the neighbourhood of the observer's position can be sketched in immediately, by keeping direction correct and converting measured distances into their correct scale values.

It is then necessary to place the alidade upon the map with the nearer end of the straight-edge touching the observer's plotted position. Using the finger-nail or pencil to prevent movement away from this point, the alidade is turned about it until a distant object, such as a signpost, gate-post, church spire, or chimney-stack is in alignment with the sighting vane. A pencil ray drawn along the straight-edge will give the direction of the object ; and the alidade is then sighted upon other distant points and a pencil ray drawn from each.

The next step is to move to a second trigonometrical station, but before leaving it is necessary to write neatly beside each ray some indication of the object it applies to.

After fixing the plane-table at the second trigonometrical

station, the map is set by placing the box compass exactly between the parallel lines drawn previously, and turning the table-top until the needle comes to rest upon the 0° line.

It should now be possible to sight the alidade upon the first trigonometrical station, and on others, with the straight-edge placed along the corresponding line of direction on the map.

With the finger or pencil upon the observer's new position to keep the straight-edge touching it, sights are now taken to all those objects for which rays were drawn at the first station, providing, of course, that they are visible. Complete pencil rays need not now be drawn, but only short rays, each cutting that drawn at the previous station which applies to the same object. By means of these intersections, the positions on the map for signpost, gate-post, and church spire are determined. Complete rays will, however, be drawn to represent the direction of additional points of the landscape to be plotted by intersection at a later stage. The sketching of detail near Station No. 2 will be done as before.

One then proceeds to each of the positions found by intersection, sets the table, and sketches in the local detail, by which time a great deal of the map-making of the section will be complete.

If a space upon the map has been missed by the intersection method, the plane-table is set at a position within the unmapped area, and rays are drawn representing directions *from* objects of known position. The point where the rays cut represents the resected position of the observer, and detail near is sketched in.

The interpolation of supplementary stations and sketching in of detail continue until the mapping of the section is complete.

In order not to confuse the reader, the question of contour drawing has been ignored in the foregoing paragraphs, but no sectional survey would be complete without it.

In order to save time the plane-tabler carries out his contour surveying simultaneously with the work so far described. For this purpose it is best for him to use some form of clinometer, and there is an instrument called the Indian Clinometer specially constructed for use with the plane-table. By using it the plane-tabler can measure the angle to the horizontal of a distant station above or below him, to draw the contours as explained on page 39.

Use of Plane Table as Applied to Territory not Previously Triangulated.

A detailed description of plane-tabling under this heading is hardly necessary if its principles have been understood. The first step is carefully to measure a base line. The table is fixed so that a plumb-bob suspended from its centre hangs vertically above one end of the base. This will be Station No. 1, No. 2 being at the other end of the line.

The base is plotted accurately to scale upon the paper, and the table set so that the station at the far end of the base is sighted correctly when the alidade has its straight-edge along the base line drawn upon the paper. Detail near the table is sketched in, and rays are drawn indicating the direction of a number of suitable distant objects. The relative positions of these are determined by intersection when other rays are drawn at the second station.

Ultimately the field is extended by resection from known points, and the map completed.

When the various sectional surveys of the island are completed, the maps embodying them are gathered together. From the information they supply the complete map of the island on a smaller scale is produced ready for printing.

In order to discover the position of the island on the earth's surface, astronomical observations are made to determine the exact latitude and longitude of one of the trigonometrical stations. A second observation will decide the relation of the whole map to true North.

When a map is made of a relatively large part of the earth's surface, there is a difficult problem to be faced, for the earth's surface being spherical, it is not simple to depict it on a flat sheet of paper. This introduces us to the subject of Map Projection.

CHAPTER FIVE

MAP PROJECTION

THE earth is nearly spherical in shape, a little flattened at each pole, like an orange, so that the polar axis, or the diameter from pole to pole, is a little shorter than the diameter from one side of the equator to the other. The former is 7900·1 miles, and the latter 7926·6 miles ; the difference is so small—about 1 in 300—that it would not be noticeable in an exact scale model. For practical purposes a globe with the geographical features of the world drawn upon its surface, such as we use at school, gives a true representation of the shape and relative size of the land and sea masses.

Map Projection is the science of transferring to a flat surface as accurate a representation as possible of the earth's surface as depicted on a globe.

If it were possible to take a sheet of transparent paper and wrap it round a globe so that it touched the latter all over without any creases, it would be simple to trace the outlines of the continents and oceans from the globe to the paper. When this was opened out flat the tracing upon it would be a map of the world, true to scale, with the shapes and relative sizes correct. Unfortunately the problem is not so easy, because without creasing we cannot put a sheet of paper around a sphere to touch it at all points.

Theoretically it is possible to take a sheet of malleable metal and to hammer it over a sphere or over a hemisphere so that it would touch all parts of the curved surface. If such a sheet of metal is actually moulded about the northern hemisphere, so that the centre of the metal bowl is touching the North Pole and the rim lies all around the Equator, then, if the outline of the continents and oceans were marked in on the hemisphere with printer's ink, they would be transferred to the inside of the metal bowl, and we should have accurate shapes and sizes. It is now for us to see what happens when the bowl is hammered flat again.

It is clear that the rim has to stretch a great deal for the bowl to become a disk. All parts have to stretch to some extent, except the part of the bowl that touched the North Pole, and the nearer the rim the greater the stretching. It follows that the sizes of countries and seas near the Equator are going to be greatly exaggerated. Measuring with a piece of string will show that the stretching in the direction parallel to the Equator is much greater than the stretching, if any, in the direction from the Pole to the Equator. Therefore the length and breadth of countries or seas are not exaggerated to the same extent, with the result that not only are the relative sizes wrong, but the shapes are wrong too.

¶There is, indeed, no way of representing on a flat surface both the correct shapes and relative sizes of masses drawn on a sphere, and the globe is the only possible true scale model of the world. If an area represented on a flat surface is very small compared with the total area of the earth, the distortion need not be great.¶ In the metal bowl, for instance, there was not very much stretching at places near the Pole, and none at the Pole itself. A piece of tracing-paper could be used to take from the globe a very accurate map of England, Ireland, or the English Channel, and the relative size of a town is so small that to make a map of one involves virtually no question of projection.

What, then, of atlas maps of large areas of the world or of continents ? Do they give us a wrong idea of the shape of Asia ? The answer is, " They do." Is the area of Greenland compared with that of Mexico different from that conveyed in an atlas map of the world ? The answer is, " Yes, unless it is a map specially made to show correct areas, in which shapes are necessarily distorted."

It will be noticed that in the attempt to explain the problems of projection by reference to the malleable metal bowl flattened out into a disk, one thing did remain correctly represented. This was the direction of all parts of the map relative to the North Pole. The true North of any one point did not alter during the flattening-out process. If the metal bowl had not been placed with its centre at the North Pole, but somewhere else on the globe, the centre of the eventual disk would have been a kind of artificial Pole, the direction of which would have remained true for all other points during and after the flattening-out. The compass bearing of an object from a stated direction, usually true North, is known as its Azimuth, and projections which show the correct bearings of all points measured from the centre of the map are called Azimuthal

Projections. An alternative name indicating the same type of projection is Zenithal.

Latitude and Longitude. Globes of the world, which are called terrestrial globes, have marked upon them meridians of longitude and parallels of latitude, usually at 10° intervals. The former are all of equal length, being drawn from pole to pole, and places on the same meridian have the same longitude, which is measured in degrees east or west of Greenwich. The parallels of latitude are circles parallel to the Equator, cutting the meridians at right angles. All places on the same parallel have the same latitude, measured north or south of the Equator, but, unlike the meridians, the parallels have not the same length. The Equator is the longest, and the others become smaller the greater their latitude, until at 90° they disappear, for 90° North and South are the poles themselves.

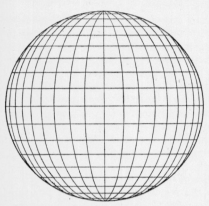

FIG. 24.—Meridians of longitude and parallels of latitude.

If we were about to draw the geographical features of the earth upon a globe, we would begin by drawing meridians of longitude and parallels of latitude upon it, probably at 10° intervals. This would provide a framework upon which the correct position for each place in the world could be determined according to its known latitude and longitude. With care and patience the whole surface of the globe could be filled in correctly, just as in Chapter I we constructed the plan of a room by plotting the position of objects by their distances from co-ordinate lines.

Now, it is impossible to represent the land and sea features of the earth upon a flat surface without distortion, and it is just as impossible to draw meridians and parallels upon a sheet of paper without errors in their form and length. If a number of atlas maps are examined it will be seen that in some cases the 10° parallels are nearer together at high latitudes than they are towards the Equator, and in other cases the opposite is true. On a terrestrial globe, however, they are the same distance apart in all latitudes, all the meridians being divided at equal intervals. Any alteration from this latter state of affairs indicates an alteration in the scale of distance along the meridians, the scale increasing as the distance along them between each pair of parallels increases.

Upon the globe the parallels become shorter as their latitude increases, and at the pole they disappear, but upon many maps they do not become shorter to the same extent, and in some all the parallels are shown the same length, the poles themselves being shown not as points, but as lines the same length as the Equator. This state of affairs indicates an increase in the scale of the parallels, the scale increasing as the total length of the parallel concerned is longer than it should be.

Upon the globe each parallel is divided equally by the 10° meridians. If upon a map a parallel is not divided equally, it shows that the scale along it is changing, being increased as the meridians become farther apart.

Effect of Alteration of Scale. Upon the errors of scale along the meridians and parallels depend the distortion of land and sea masses drawn upon their framework. Suppose, for example, that a particular island was of such a size and shape that it exactly fitted into the space between two parallels and two meridians [Fig. 25 (1)]. If the scale along the parallels at the position of the island is doubled, but the meridian scale remains the same, the island is stretched twofold in one direction and doubled in area [Fig. 25 (2)]. If the scale along the meridians at the position of the island is doubled, but the parallel scale remains the same, the island is stretched twofold in the other direction and again doubled in area [Fig. 25 (3)].

Orthomorphic or Correct Shape Projection. If both scales are doubled, the island is stretched twofold both in length and breadth, and the area quadrupled, but the equal increase of size in each direction does not alter the shape [Fig. 25 (4)]. This fact is of the greatest importance, because it means that any projection which keeps the meridian and parallel scales equal to one another at all points of the map, no matter how they alter together from point to point, maintains the correct

shape of small islands, lakes, and bays. For instance, around
the shores of a continent on this kind of map all the small
features will be the correct shape. Unfortunately they will be
shown on different scales at different parts of the continent
so that the shape of the latter will be inaccurate.

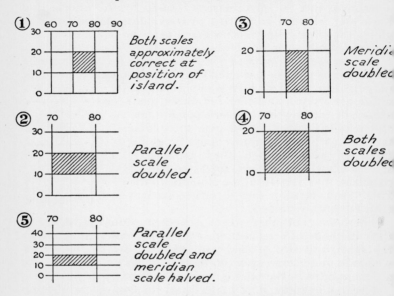

FIG. 25.—Showing the effect of alteration of scale along meridians
and parallels.

Projections which maintain the true shape of small areas in
this way are called Orthomorphic Projections.

Homolographic or Equal-Area Projections. If, however, at
the position of the above island one of the scales were doubled
and the other halved, the island would be shown excessively
distorted, but the area would be correct, for by doubling its
length and halving its width the area is not affected [Fig.
25 (5)]. This fact is also of great importance, because it
means that any projection which alters the meridian and
parallel scale in inverse proportion, maintains the correct
area of land and sea features all over the map.

These projections are called Equal-Area or Homolographic.

Distortion of Shape Due to Sheering. Errors in the scale of meridians and parallels are often accompanied by errors of the angle at which they intersect. On the globe the angle is 90°, but on maps it sometimes varies at different points. As a result of this the small shapes formed by the intersecting lines are different from the corresponding shapes on the globe, the effect being most marked near the boundary of the map (Fig. 26).

How to Make Allowances for Projection. To many readers it will have already occurred that a very quick method of judging distortion in a map is to observe the difference in size and shape of these small areas, enclosed by the intersecting meridians and parallels. It is a good plan to become familiar with their form upon a globe, noticing that although they are exactly similar anywhere between the same pair of parallels, they vary from the Equator to the Pole. Any variation due to projection can then be quickly judged.

FIG. 26.—Distortion of shape due to sheering.

There are many methods of projection, differing widely in their methods of construction, and having different errors in the shape and size of land and sea features. If the reader wishes to understand each thoroughly, books upon the subject are mentioned in the bibliography at the end of this book.

For our purpose it is unnecessary to enquire so deeply. This chapter attempts only to prevent the reader from being misled by the shapes, relative sizes, and distances represented in ordinary atlas and wall-maps. If well produced, these show the method of projection upon them, but it is a fact that to most people this information has no meaning and is rarely noticed. In order to make allowance for distortion, it is necessary to understand how the scales along the parallels and meridians alter in each projection, and this information is provided in Chapter Six.

The Principles of Map Projection. The systems by which the meridians of longitude and parallels of latitude are drawn on a sheet of paper to provide the framework of a map can be divided into two distinct types, the Geometrical and the Non-Geometrical.

Geometrical Projections. Let us suppose that we have a hollow glass globe with the meridians and parallels drawn upon its surface. If at its centre is placed a point of light, a shadow network of lines will be thrown upon a paper screen placed in contact with the globe in one of three ways :

1. As a flat surface touching at one point only.
2. As a cylindrical surface touching at all points along a great circle.[1]
3. As a conical surface touching the sphere at all points along a small circle.[1]

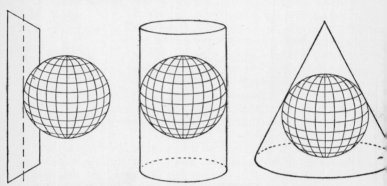

Fig. 27.—Three ways in which a paper screen can be made to touch a glass globe.

The shadow of the meridians and parallels obtained in this way is a Geometrical Projection, and any system of map projection which has meridians and parallels drawn as they would appear if a shadow experiment were carried out is called a Geometrical Projection.

[1] *Great and Small Circles.* A Great Circle is an imaginary circle the plane of which passes through the centre of the world. A cut along it would result in two equal hemispheres. The Equator is an example, and each meridian is half of one, but there is an infinite number of additional ones intersecting the meridians and parallels at varying angles. The shortest line joining any two points on the surface of the world is part of a Great Circle, a matter of great importance to navigators of the sea and air.

A Small Circle is an imaginary circle the plane of which does not pass through the centre of the world, as in the case of any parallel not the Equator. A cut along it results in two parts unequal in size.

The first method—of placing a flat screen in contact with
a sphere—is also used to produce projections with the point
of light moved farther from the screen.   For explanation let
us suppose that the paper is held vertically, touching the globe
at its North Pole, with the polar axis, or line joining the poles,

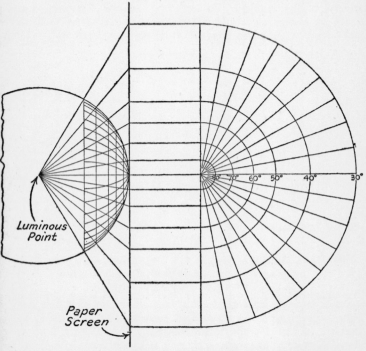

Fig. 28.—Projection obtained on a flat screen with a luminous
point at the centre of a hollow globe.

a horizontal direction.   It is clear that, with the light at the
centre of the sphere, a portion of the Northern Hemisphere
will be projected rather like a spider's web in appearance.
The rest of the Northern Hemisphere, lying near to the
Equator, will be projected beyond the edge of the paper screen
and the Equator to infinity (Fig. 28).
If the light is moved along the polar axis to the South Pole

the spider-web shadow will get smaller, and more of th
meridians and parallels will fall upon the screen, the Equato
itself appearing if the screen is large enough (Fig. 29).

Upon the light being moved outside the sphere on a con
tinuation of the polar axis, the shadow of part of the Souther:
Hemisphere will be superimposed upon the shadow of th·
Northern Hemisphere. In order to remove this complicatio·
it will be necessary to cut the globe in two around its Equato·
and consider only the projection of the northern half. If th

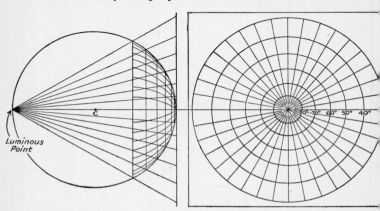

Fig. 29.—Projection obtained on a flat screen with a luminous
point on the opposite surface of a hollow globe.
(Stereographic Projection.)

light be moved an infinite distance away, so that the rays
light falling upon the screen are parallel to the polar axis, th·
shadow of the Northern Hemisphere will appear with ever·
parallel exactly the same size as it is upon the globe (Fig. 30
These projections upon a flat surface are similar to th·
projection obtained by the inaugural experiment with th·
malleable metal bowl described on page 56. The bearin
from the North Pole for any point on the earth's surface i
shown correctly on the map, and the projection is therefor
Azimuthal or Zenithal.

In the above explanations the point of contact was the Nort
Pole, so that the projections obtained were Polar Azimutha
If the point of contact had been some other point upon th·

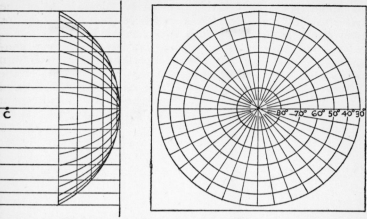

FIG. 30.—Projection obtained on a flat screen with a luminous point at an infinite distance away from the screen and beyond a portion of a hollow globe.   (Orthographic Projection.)

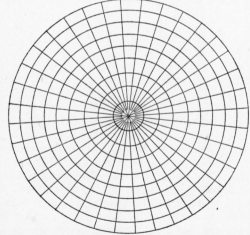

FIG. 31.—Polar Azimuthal Equal-Area Projection in which the meridians and parallels are drawn by mathematical means so that their respective scales alter in inverse proportion.   The spaces enclosed by the lines are therefore the same area as on the globe, but the shapes are wrong.

E

surface of the globe, the spider-web effect would not have
been obtained. The meridians would not have been straight
lines radiating from the central point, nor would the parallels
have been concentric circles about that point. Nevertheless,
these Non-Polar Azimuthal Projections must be remembered,
for certain of them are used for atlas maps.

Non-Geometrical Projections. In practice it is often necessary
to construct the framework of meridians and parallels in a
form which differs from that obtained by any method of
shadow projection. In order to make an equal area map, the
scales along the meridians and parallels must alter in inverse

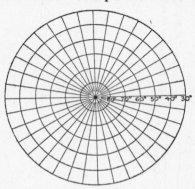

FIG. 32.—Polar Azimuthal Equidistant Projection in which the parallels
    are arranged by mathematical means to divide the radiating
    meridians into lengths which equal the corresponding lengths on
    the globe. All distances measured from the Pole are thus correct

proportion (page 60), and if a geometrical projection is adjusted
for this purpose, it becomes non-geometrical (Fig. 31).

Similarly, if it is intended to construct a polar map in which
all distances measured from the Pole are true, the parallels
must divide the radiating meridians into lengths which equal
the corresponding lengths on the globe. This can be arranged
if a geometrical projection is adjusted, but the result is non-
geometrical (Fig. 32).

Equal-Area and Equidistant Projections can also be made
by adjustment of the meridians and parallels thrown upon the
screen when it touches the globe cylindrically or conically.

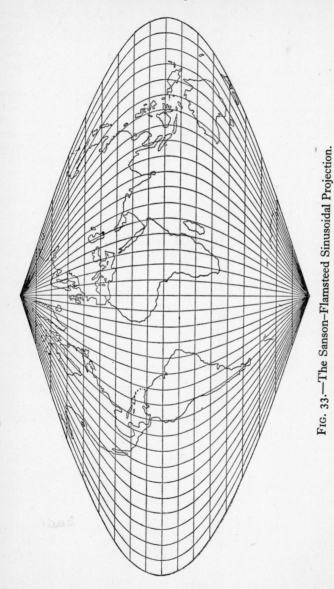

FIG. 33.—The Sanson–Flamsteed Sinusoidal Projection.

Many maps are constructed, however, by systems which bear no resemblance to geometrical projections. The meridians and parallels are drawn in a form determined by mathematical methods. In the Sanson–Flamsteed Sinusoidal projection (Fig. 33), for instance, all the parallels are horizontal straight lines the same length as those on the globe, equally divided by the meridians, so that the scale along them is correct. The vertical distance between the parallels is the same as the distance between them on the globe. It follows that any portion of the world lying between two parallels has the same base and vertical height on the map as it has on the globe. This makes the projection Equal-Area. Distortion of shape is caused by all the meridians except the central one being curved. They do not cross the parallels at right angles, and their scale is incorrect. Distortion is least in the middle of the map, and the projection is valuable for representing those parts of the world which lie partly above and partly below the Equator, such as South America, Africa, or the Pacific Ocean.

CHAPTER SIX

CHARACTERISTICS OF THE COMMONER
PROJECTIONS

IT is not the writers' intention to describe fully each method of projection. The previous chapter explained that no map of a large area of the world gives a true representation of both shape and relative area. This present chapter attempts to list the various accuracies and inaccuracies of the commoner projections, so that allowance can be made for their errors when map reading.

SECTION I. AZIMUTHAL OR ZENITHAL PROJECTIONS.

In the Polar Azimuthal or Zenithal Projections the central point of the map is either the North or the South Pole. The meridians are straight lines radiating from the Pole like the spokes of a wheel, and the parallels are concentric circles with the Pole as centre. At the Pole and near to it there is very little error of size or shape. Distortion occurs in latitudes distant from the Pole, according to the errors in the meridian and parallel scales which are described below.

In Non-Polar Azimuthal or Zenithal Projections the central point of the map is not the North or South Pole, and the meridians and parallels have a form differing from that described above. At the centre of the map and near to it there is again very little error of size or shape. To apply the errors of scale described below to non-polar projections, they must not be attributed to the meridians and parallels. One has to imagine straight radiating lines and concentric circles, and apply the errors of scale to them.

A. Geometrical Types.

The Gnomonic Projection (Fig. 28). Scales are correct only at the Pole.

Along the radiating meridians the scale increases rapidly, especially within 60° of the Equator.

That along the parallels increases, but not to the same extent as along the meridians.

The projection is therefore neither Equal-Area nor Ortho-morphic, and is only used occasionally for polar regions.

The Stereographic Projection (Fig. 29). Away from the Pole the scale along the meridians and that along the parallels increase in the same proportion. At any place on the map the two scales are equal.

The map is therefore orthomorphic, but areas are exag-gerated as latitude diminishes. Distortion is less than in the Gnomonic Projection, and this method is sometimes used for making non-polar maps of the world in hemispheres.

Sir Henry James's Projection. This projection is neither Orthomorphic nor Equal-Area, but compromises between the errors of shape and size to produce a map of minimum total error.

The Orthographic Projection (Fig. 30). The scale along the meridians diminishes away from the centre of the map, but that along the parallels is correct in all latitudes. The method is therefore not orthomorphic, and areas diminish as they recede from the Pole.

B. Non-Geometrical Types.

Azimuthal Equidistant Projection (Fig. 32). The scale along the meridians is made exactly true, so that all distances measured from the Pole are correct. The scale along the parallels increases away from the Pole. The projection is used for maps of polar exploration.

Azimuthal Equal-Area Projection (Fig. 31). The scales along the meridians and parallels are made to alter in inverse pro-portion, the former being diminished and the latter increased away from the Pole. The projection is therefore Equal-Area, but shows the shape of countries excessively distorted except near the centre.

This projection is better known as *Lambert's Azimuthal Equivalent Projection*, or *Lambert's Zenithal Equal-Area Projection*.

SECTION 2. CYLINDRICAL PROJECTIONS.

The parallels of every type of cylindrical projection are straight horizontal lines of the same length, equally divided by the meridians, which are straight vertical lines.

The scale continues the same along each of the parallels, but is different for each one. Only on the Equator is the scale correct. The other parallels on the globe become smaller as they approach the Poles, so their equal length under this projection means an ever-increasing scale.

Scale errors along the meridians vary with the particular type of projection.

A. Geometrical Type.

Cylindrical Equal-Area Projection. In this projection the scale along the meridians decreases with latitude, in the same ratio as that along the parallels increases.

The projection is therefore Equal-Area, but distorts the shape of countries in high latitudes excessively. It is only used for maps of equatorial regions.

B. Non-Geometrical Types.

Cylindrical Equidistant Projection. The scale along the meridians is made exactly true. All

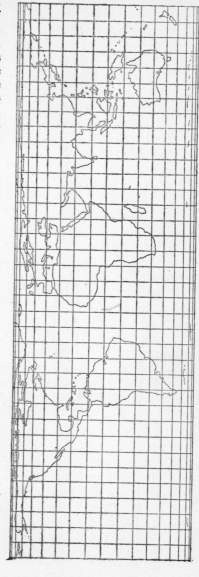

FIG. 34.—The Cylindrical Equal-Area Projection.

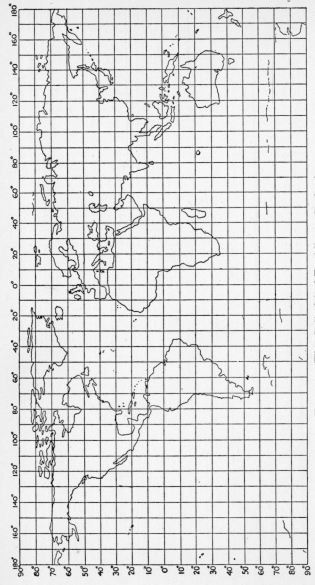

FIG. 35.—The Cylindrical Equidistant Projection.

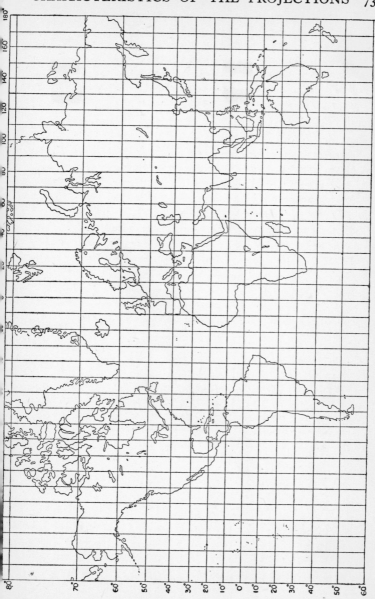

FIG. 36.—Mercator's Projection.

distances measured along them are correct, and the parallels
are the same distance apart.

The map is not Equal-Area, and distortion in high latitudes
makes the map useful only for equatorial regions.

Mercator's Projection. The scale along the meridians is
made to increase in proportion to the scale along the parallels,
so that at any point of the map the scale is the same in every
direction. The map is therefore orthomorphic, but areas
increase rapidly as latitude increases. Mercator's Projection
is the most popular for maps of the world, and accounts for
the wrong ideas about the shape of the continents possessed
by people who do not understand the problems of projection.

The following is a table showing the exaggeration of area
in varying latitudes :

Latitude.	*Extent of Increase.*
0° (the Equator)	Nil.
45°	Areas doubled.
60°	Areas 4 times too large.
75°	Areas nearly 16 times too large.
80°	Areas more than 33 times too large.
90° (the Poles)	Areas increased to infinity.

For practical purposes latitudes above 81° North and below
70° South are omitted.

On Mercator's maps there is usually a special type of plain
scale to show the scale of miles along the parallels in different
latitudes, while the increase in the scale along the meridians
can be judged from the intervals at which the parallels cross
them. These increase with latitude, whilst on a globe, of
course, they are equal.

The true compass bearing between any two places in the
world is shown by the straight line between them on a
Mercator map—an advantage of the greatest importance to
navigators of the sea and air. Sea-charts are frequently
projected on Mercator's Projection for this reason.

SECTION 3.   CONICAL PROJECTIONS.

The meridians of a conical projection are straight lines
running from the top to the bottom of the map. If in the
Northern Hemisphere, they are closer together at the top, and

if produced would meet at a point above the edge, which would be the North Pole. In the Southern hemisphere they converge in similar manner towards the South Pole, below the bottom edge of the map. The parallels are concentric arcs of circles drawn about the point to which the meridians converge.

No geometrical type of conical projection provides a map suitable for practical use.

Non-Geometrical Types.

Simple Conical Projections with one Standard Parallel. In this projection the scale is made correct along all the meridians,

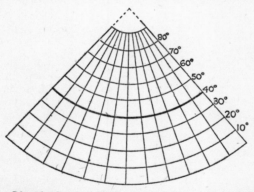

FIG. 37.—Simple Conical Projection with one Standard parallel.

so that the distances between the parallels are the same. The scale is also true along one parallel, usually the middle one, called the Standard Parallel; but the scale along the others increases as they recede from it, both towards the top and towards the bottom of the map.

The projection is therefore neither Equal-Area nor Orthomorphic, and is not suitable for high latitudes. It is useful for maps of countries which extend in a direction from West to East and do not cover more than 30° of latitude.

Simple Conical Projection with Two Standard Parallels. This projection differs from the previous one only in having two parallels along which the scale is true, instead of one.

Above and below them the parallel scale increases, but between them it diminishes.

The advantage of this arrangement is that the amount of error at the top and bottom of the map is less. It provides good maps of Europe, Asia, North America, and Australia, and is also used extensively for making atlas maps of individual countries.

Conical Equal-Area Projection. The two previous projections can each be modified to make the distance between the parallels—*i.e.*, the meridian scale—vary in inverse proportion to the parallel scale. This results in areas being shown correctly.

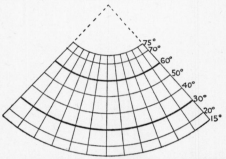

FIG. 38.—Conical Projection with two Standard Parallels
(Northern Hemisphere).

Conical Orthomorphic Projection. This projection is the opposite of the previous one. The meridian and parallel scales change in direct, and not inverse proportion, so that at any point of the map the two are equal. Small shapes, such as those of lakes, bays, islands, etc., are shown correctly, but exaggeration of area occurs above and below the standard parallel. If there are two of these, areas between them are diminished.

SECTION 4. OTHER NON-GEOMETRICAL PROJECTIONS.

Under this head are included important projections frequently used for map-making which do not come within the Azimuthal, Cylindrical or Conical classifications. The shadow method of projection has no bearing on their construction. The parallels and meridians are drawn in various ways, and each projection has its advantages together with its dis-advantages.

The Polyconic Projection. The scale along the central and vertically straight meridian is true. Suppose that a series of simple conical projections were drawn, with the standard parallel of the first at 10° latitude, the standard parallel of the second at 20° latitude, and so on, and the distances between all the parallels the same as that upon the globe. Now, a composite map made up by taking the standard parallel out

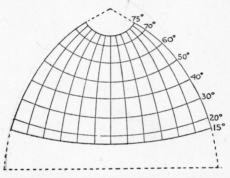

FIG. 39.—The Polyconic Projection.

of each of the above series, and placing it upon a central and vertical straight meridian of true scale, will give the parallels and central meridian of the polyconic projection. To find the position of the other meridians it is necessary to mark off on each parallel the positions where the meridians crossed in the projection for which it was the standard one. The polyconic meridians are drawn to cross the parallels at these positions.

Owing to the nature of the construction, however, these will be curved lines, and the scale along them increases the farther east or west of the central meridian they become.

Near the central meridian shapes and sizes are fairly accurate, so that for countries not extending much beyond 30° on each side of the central meridian the projection is very useful.

Sanson–Flamsteed Sinusoidal Projection. The parallels of latitude in this projection are horizontal straight lines with the scale along them correct. The meridians therefore divide each parallel into equal lengths (see Figs. 33 and 40).

FIG. 40.—Sanson–Flamsteed Sinusoidal Projection.

The scale along the central and vertically straight meridian is also true, which makes the vertical distance between the parallels correct.

All other meridians are curved lines, the scale along which becomes greater as they near the east and west boundaries of the map.

Each small quadrilateral formed by the intersecting parallels and meridians has the correct area, because its top and bottom sides, and its vertical height, are exactly the same as they would be upon a globe of equal scale. The projection is therefore Equal-Area, but distortion is excessive everywhere except in the middle of the map.

Africa, South America, and the Pacific Ocean are usually mapped on this projection, which is seldom used for anything else.

Bonne's Equal-Area Projection. This is a modified conical projection resembling the Sanson–Flamsteed Sinusoidal in

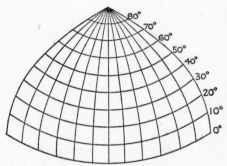

FIG. 41.—Bonne's Equal-Area Projection.

certain ways. For instance, the scale along the parallels is true, but their form is that of concentric arcs of circles. The scale along the central and vertically straight meridian is true, which makes the vertical distance between each pair of parallels equal and correct.

The projection is Equal-Area, but because all meridians but the central one are curved and of varying scales, it is not orthomorphic, except near the central meridian.

It serves very well for areas not near the Poles and not extending far to east and west.

Mollweide's Equal-Area Projection. The parallels of latitude are horizontal straight lines, but the distance between them decreases slightly from the Equator to the Pole. Near the Equator they are wider apart than they would be on a globe of the same scale, and near the Poles they are closer together.

This means that the scale along the central and vertically straight meridian is not constant, but diminishes with latitude. The scale along other meridians increases to the east and west of the central one, and they are curved.

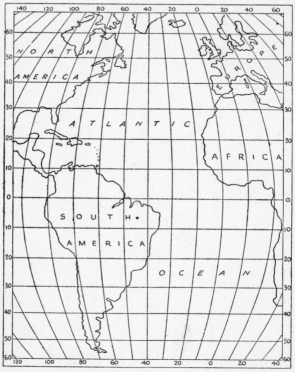

FIG. 42.—Mollweide's Equal-Area Projection.

The scale along each of the parallels is constant, but increases slightly with latitude.

The projection has the advantage of being Equal-Area, but distortion of shape is considerable. Only at two points is it orthomorphic, roughly at one-quarter and three-quarters the distance along the central meridian.

Mollweide's projection is sometimes used to represent hemispheres or smaller areas.

Projection by Rectangular Co-ordinates. This projection, often called Cassini's, is of great importance, because it is used in the 1-inch Ordnance Survey map of England.

In Chapter I it was explained that, when making a plan

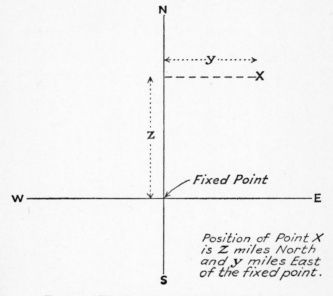

FIG. 43.—The Principle of Cassini's Projection.

of a room, the position of an object is determined by measuring its distance from two walls, and it is plotted by measuring scale distances from co-ordinate lines.

A map of a country can be projected by similar means, providing that its area is not large compared with the surface of the earth. For the Ordnance Map of England a meridian passing through Delamere Forest in Cheshire is chosen as the vertical co-ordinate. The position of any place in the country can be determined by finding the length of the perpendicular drawn from it to the meridian, and the distance along the

F

latter between the foot of the perpendicular and some fixed point. The horizontal co-ordinate is, of course, the line at right angles to the meridian at the fixed point.

For convenience in the case of the English 1-inch-to-the-mile Ordnance Maps, these distances are converted to measurements north and east of a point situated in the sea southwest of Land's End. Upon the maps are drawn horizontal and vertical straight lines at distances apart representing 5000 yards, each marked in the margin with its distance north or east of the point near Land's End. They do not indicate latitude and longitude, and must not be confused with parallels and meridians, to which they are not even parallel. Their purpose is to indicate the position of any point relative to the co-ordinates.

Owing to the small relative area of England, this method of projection provides a very accurate map. On the coast of Norfolk, where the error is greatest, it is only about 1 in 1000, which is less than possible errors in map-printing.

CHAPTER SEVEN

THE EARLY MAP-MAKERS

HISTORY so often seems to the reader a list of dates better forgotten, of names that cannot be made alive, of events that have nothing to do with the modern world. When, however, one takes a subject such as map-making, and traces its history from the earliest days down to the present, and sees what influence dates and men and events have had upon it, then history becomes alive, being indeed the record of people who did things that still affect the world. We shall see that the old names famous in cartography or map-making—Ptolemy, Mercator, and Saxton—still live in the Ordnance sheet that we buy before setting off for a holiday.

The two essentials of map-making—a method of determining the position of a point on the earth's surface so that it can always be found by anyone, and a knowledge of the shape of the world and its approximate size—both owe their foundations to the men of what we call "the ancient world". The Babylonians, before the Romans, divided the circle of the sky into 360°, and each degree into 60 minutes, and each minute into 60 seconds. (They had a system of counting based on sixties and figures that would divide into sixties, as we have one based on hundreds as well as the remains of the old Babylonian system.) They were also responsible for the division of the day into twelve hours, and the splitting up of the hours into minutes and seconds. This division of the sky enabled a place on the earth's surface to have its position plotted in relation to the stars, and so a constant position to be given to it which did not depend on description or measurement of the earth.

The attainment of the second essential—a knowledge of the shape and size of the earth—was due to the Greeks, who, one must remember, in the ancient world did not live only in Greece, but in Asia Minor, Egypt, Africa, and Italy, just as to-day many Englishmen do not live in England, but throughout the Empire and in foreign countries. It was an African Greek, Eratosthenes of Cyrene, in Libya—a man who was the keeper of the greatest library of the old world, at Alexandria—who realised that the world was round, and who worked out a measurement of its size which was almost correct. However, another astronomer who came later, Posidonius, thought Eratosthenes had made a mistake, and corrected him. The great Ptolemy, of whom we shall learn in a moment, adopted Posidonius' conclusions, and the error lasted until as late as 1700. It is curious to think that, though the charts of the Mediterranean made in the Middle Ages corrected the work of Posidonius and Ptolemy, whose measurements of that sea were found to be wrong by practical experience, yet, in the opinion of a modern geographer, Columbus did not apply the knowledge that had been gained by the Mediterranean chart-makers in making his estimate of the size of the whole world. It will be remembered that Columbus was looking for another way to the Indies and China, and these lands, on Ptolemy's reckoning, should have been found somewhere near where Columbus actually discovered the American continent. If the explorer had realised the much greater distance that it really was from Europe to the East Indies across the Atlantic, it is more than possible that he would never have started.

Ptolemy was a Greek of Egypt, who lived in the second century, about 300 years after Eratosthenes and 150 after Posidonius. He applied the discovery of the Babylonians and that of Posidonius to geography. He did not draw maps himself, but published a book called *Geographia*, from the descriptions in which maps were afterwards constructed. This book was re-discovered in the Middle Ages, and a Latin edition appeared in 1475. Upon it were based all the maps that were brought out until, in the eighteenth century, accurate measurements of the earth's surface were made, and the first modern maps, on these measurements, appeared.

In spite of Eratosthenes, the usual opinion before Ptolemy among the Greeks, who were the outstanding enquirers of the ancient world, was that the earth was a disc, entirely surrounded by a great river called Oceanus. Greece was thought to be roughly in the middle of the disc, the western boundary of which was beyond the Pillars of Hercules, which we now know as the Straits of Gibraltar. To the south, Africa was known as far as the desert ; east, the line of the known world ran roughly·along the line of the river Indus, in India, down which Alexander the Great had floated with his fleet, returning from his conquests in Persia and India. North and north-east little was known beyond the countries round the Mediterranean, and the Black and Caspian Seas. The sun was supposed to pass at night right underneath this flat world, on the edge of which the Greeks placed their fabled lands, such as Elysium and the Fortunate Isles.

Ptolemy's book showed an advance on this knowledge. In *Geographia* we read of the British Isles (Ptolemy calls Great Britain Albion and Ireland Iverna). Scandinavia he knew

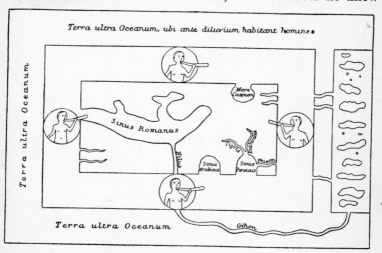

Fig. 44.—Cosmas' Map.

and the islands in its neighbourhood. He realised that there were lands beyond the African desert. North-east he describes the Volga correctly, and knows that the Caspian is an inland sea. East he knows of India, the Malay peninsula, and China : " far away," he says, " towards the north, there is a land containing a great city from which silk is exported, both raw and spun and woven into textures."

After the fall of the western Roman Empire, the growth and spread of Christianity led to the production of a different sort of map. Jerusalem, not Greece, was thought of as the centre of the world, and all places were related to it. Since the Bible gave no authority for Ptolemy's view that the world was round, it was again shown as flat. Cosmas, a monk of the sixth century, backed up this opinion with the argument— quite correct so far as the facts went, but wrong in respect of

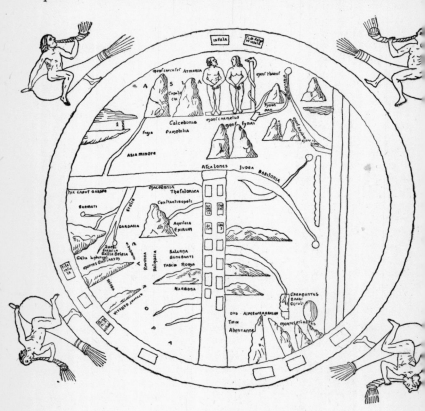

FIG. 45.—Turin Map.

the inferences drawn from them : " If it be a sphere, then there must actually be people standing feet to feet," and he attempted to satisfy his followers by drawing a picture of four men standing " feet to feet ", which he thought was a sufficiently convincing *reductio ad absurdum*.

His is the oldest Christian map. Round the flat earth is the ocean stream, from which flow the four rivers of Paradise, and then the outer " earth beyond the ocean where men dwelt before the Flood ".

In Turin there is an eighth-century map, with the world divided into Asia, Africa, and Europe. Adam and Eve stand at the top ; to the right of Adam lies Armenia and the Caucasus ; to the left of Eve are Mount Lebanon, the river Jordan, Sidon, and Mesopotamia. At their feet lie Mount Carmel, Jerusalem, and Babylon. In Europe a few places are named such as Constantinople, Italy, France. Britannia and Scotland are islands in the encircling sea. Africa is suitably represented by the Nile.

After another two centuries we have the Anglo-Saxon map, which is in the British Museum. Here is a mixture of Biblical and classical knowledge. Jerusalem and Bethlehem are in their place, and the Pillars of Hercules stand at the entrance to the Mediterranean Sea. The British Isles are still distorted, and quantities of little, unnamed islands lie about the north of Scotland. In the extreme east lies an enormous Ceylon ; in the north-east corner of Asia is drawn a magnificent lion with mane and circling tail, with the words around him : " Here lions abound." Africa as usual is made up of the Nile, Alexandria at its mouth, and its source in a lake.

About 1300 we have the *Mappa Mundi*, by Richard of Haldingham, which is in Hereford Cathedral. (The word " map ", by the way, comes from the Latin *mappa*, meaning a napkin or cloth, because the earliest ones were drawn on cloths.) Jerusalem is in the centre, and the Crucifixion is there depicted. At the top is the last Judgment, with the good and bad folk divided on either side. Adam and Eve are there, so are the Pillars of Hercules, Scylla and Charybdis, the Red Sea coloured red, the Nile and the Mountains of the Moon, strange beasts and stranger men.

All these maps show the religious and symbolic attitude towards cartography which succeeded the scientific outlook of Ptolemy. The latter wanted to give a description of the world as it really was ; the maps we have described aimed at showing how all the things and places God had made were related, and so everything was grouped round Jerusalem, no trouble being taken to make the maps exact.

Stimulated by the invention of printing and the expansion
of learning which we call the Renaissance, the cartographers

Fig. 46.—The Anglo-Saxon Map of the World, drawn about A.D. 990

of the late Middle Ages groped their way towards the idea of a
map that should combine pictorial qualities with an accurate

representation of the world as it was then known ; and one of the first results of the New Learning, so far as map-making was concerned, was a revival of interest in Ptolemy himself. As we have said, the first mediæval edition of his book was published in 1475. An interesting map based on him was produced in 1508 by John Ruysch at Rome, the first printed map to show the discoveries of Columbus, though a map of 1507, called the Waldseemüller map, showed part of the New World, and was the first to use the name America, a word derived from the explorer Amerigo Vespucci. In addition, this map showed the discoveries of the Portuguese on the African coast, gave to India its correct shape and position, and for the first time since Ptolemy had written his book over 1300 years before, furnished new information regarding the east and interior of Asia.

The 1513 edition of Ptolemy shows a recognisable portion of the New World : the north and part of the east coast of South America, the east coast of Central and North America, and the islands of Hispaniola (shared to-day by the republics of Hayti and Santo Domingo), Cuba, and the West Indies.

Editions of Ptolemy continued to be published, and, in consequence of the new discoveries, the science of cartography became very popular during the sixteenth century. Many map-makers appeared, progress was rapid as production changed from engraving on wood to engraving on copper, and maps became at the same time more accurate and more ornamental. The Dark Ages of map-making were over.

CHAPTER EIGHT

DUTCHMEN AND FRENCHMEN

THE sixteenth century in cartography is the century of the Dutch and Flemish map-makers, of Mercator, Ortelius, and the three families of the Blaeus, the Janssons, and the Hondius, as well as of many lesser names with whom we need not concern ourselves. The maps that these men made can be seen not only in museums : specimens of them can be bought quite cheaply by those who love maps and can afford only a little money. If money is not available, then make friends with a bookseller who deals in old maps, and he will, if he is a true lover of books, show his collection to you because he likes to find others who are interested in the same things as he is. It would be a good thing if a collection of these old maps were formed in every school : perhaps the teaching of geography would then become more interesting. Regard this chapter not as dry history, but as the story of men who were beginning to understand that the world was much bigger and more complicated than their fathers had thought ; who lived at a time when trade was expanding quickly, as a result of which merchants by land and pilots by sea had to have maps and charts to guide them ; and who combined with their careful and accurate map-making a love of beauty and a craftsmanship that led them to make their maps objects of art in which subsequent generations can take delight. The colour plates in Humphreys's *Old Decorative Maps and Charts*, the reproductions in Nordenskiöld's *Facsimile Atlas*, and the illustrations in the other books mentioned in the list on page 138, any of which your Public Librarian will get for you on loan, will show you a great number of these maps.

Mercator's name is known to us all because of Mercator's projection, which is described in an earlier chapter. He was born in 1512, at Rupelmonde, near Antwerp, the son of a shoemaker. Mercator is the Latinised form of the name de Cramer or Krämer. An uncle, who saw his skill with precision instruments, sent him to the University of Louvain, and when he left there he set up in business as a maker of mathematical and astronomical instruments, adding the drawing, engraving, and illuminating of maps as a sideline.

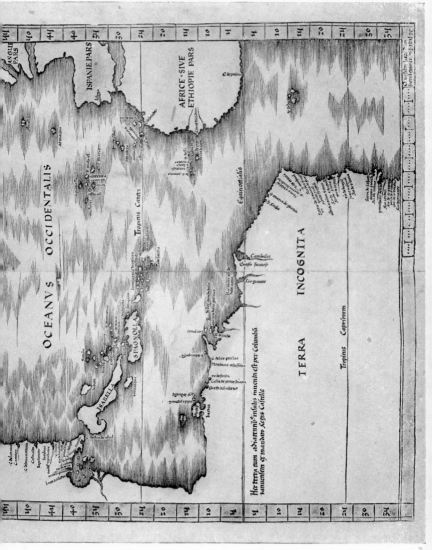

PTOLEMY'S
MAP OF
1513.

In 1564, working on material sent him by a friend in England, he drew a large and accurate map of the British Isles on a scale of 1 inch to 14 miles, which was, however, never engraved. It was not long ago discovered at Breslau, and has now been reproduced by photography.

A few years later he produced his chart, only one copy of the original issue of which exists, in the Bibliothèque Nationale at Paris, drawn on the famous projection (see page 74). Humphreys says : " Mercator's chart stands alone in map history, isolated from the many other works he accomplished. It was not heralded by any previous announcement, and no mention appears to have been made of it in his subsequent publications. He was a prophet without honour in his own time. Even after his death his successor did not think ' the projection ' of sufficient account to give it a place in the *Atlas*. We know, however, that early in the seventeenth century the French seaport of Dieppe was the principal depot for the publication and sale of nautical charts, and that those then sold at Dieppe were on Mercator's projection. Modern geography and map-making really date from Mercator."

He died in 1594 ; for the last ten years of his life he had been busy collecting and making maps for his *Atlas*, which it is thought was meant as the first volume of a great encyclopædia of the sciences. He died, however, before the *Atlas* was published, and it was left to his son to bring it out. Later on, the plates of all the maps and charts that he had published over a period of more than thirty years were bought by Jodocus Hondius of Amsterdam, who in 1606 brought out an edition with fifty new maps, which were engraved by Peter Kaerius, whom we shall meet again. In the course of 75 years Hondius and his successors at Amsterdam brought out fifty editions of the Mercator *Atlas*.

This was the first occasion on which the word was applied to a volume of maps, and one supposes that Mercator meant it to signify that his book contained the whole world within its covers, as the giant Atlas was once said to bear the world upon his shoulders. Other map publishers used different words. Ortelius, and later John Speed, called their collections *Theatrum* or Theatre, meaning display, and other words, such as *Speculum*, were used ; but Atlas stuck, and we have it to-day, to remind us of the greatest geographer of them all.

A friend and rival of Mercator was Abraham Ortelius, born on the banks of the Scheldt near Mercator's birthplace. So fond were the two men of each other that it is said Mercator held back from publication the collection of maps he had formed in order that the sales of his friend's work, the *Theatrum Orbis Terrarum*, which was the first real Atlas as we understand the term, meaning a collection of maps covering the world, should not be affected. It was published in 1570. Abraham Ortel (as he was really called) did not draw many of the maps himself, but reproduced the work of other cartographers. The book originated because Hooftman, an Antwerp merchant, had begun to collect maps. As his collection increased and he became more and more interested in it, he found the task of rolling and unrolling his large maps a nuisance, and so he commissioned Ortel to purchase as many single-sheet maps as he could find and bind them into a single book. The latter put together about thirty maps for Hooftman, and then decided that the volume should be published for the benefit of the public, and so he began work on the *Theatrum*. After its first issue in 1570, many other editions appeared up to 1612, including an English edition in 1606.

Willem Janszoon Blaeu was of a later generation than the two friends. He was a Dutchman, born in 1571, and he began work in Amsterdam as a joiner's apprentice. A little later, through an introduction, he got to know Tycho Brahe, the great Danish astronomer, and lived with him for two years on the island of Hveen, where Brahe had his observatory. What he learned there while acting as assistant to Brahe enabled him to return to Amsterdam about 1597 and start in business as a maker of mathematical instruments and as an engraver and printer of maps.

He decided that under his own roof he would have a place where all the processes of map-making could be carried on efficiently, and where the arts that he practised could have free scope. He died about forty years later, soon after the States-General had appointed him map-maker to the Republic. His business passed to his two sons, John and Cornelius Blaeu, and later to his grandson, all of whom inherited the official title. The following description of the great firm at work is quoted from the biography of the elder Blaeu by E. L. Stevenson.

" ' On the Blumengracht,' says Filips von Zesen, in his description of the city of Amsterdam, ' near the third bridge, and the third alley, may be found the greatly renowned printing house of John Blaeu, Counsellor and Magistrate, of the city. It is furnished with nine type presses, named after the nine Muses, six presses for copperplate printing, and a type foundry. The entire establishment on the canal, with the adjoining house in which the proprietor lives, is 75 feet in breadth, and stretches along the east side of a cross street 135 feet, or with the attached house 150 feet. Fronting on the canal is a room with cases in which the copper plates are kept, from which the Atlases, the Book of the Cities of the Netherlands and of foreign countries, also the Mariner's Atlases and other choice books are printed, and which must have cost a ton of gold. Next to this first room is a press room used for plate printing, and opening upon the cross street referred to above is a place where the type, from which impressions have been made, was washed ; then follows in order the room for book printing, which resembles a long hall with windows on either side. In the extreme rear is a room in which the type and certain other materials used in printing are stored. Opposite this store room is a stairway leading to a small room above, which is set apart for the use of the proof-readers, where first and second impressions are carefully looked over, and the errors corrected which have been made by the typesetters. In front of this last designated room is a long table or bench on which the final prints are placed as soon as they are brought from the press, and where they are left for a considerable time. In the story above is a table for the same purpose just indicated, at the extreme end of which, and over the room occupied by the proof-readers, is the type foundry wherein the letters used in the printing of the various languages are moulded.

" ' The foundation of this splendid building was laid in the year 1636, by John Blaeu's oldest son Willem Blaeu, and on the 13th of the fall month of the following year the printing establishment was here set in order. The original founder of the printing house, who died in the following year, was John Blaeu's art loving father Willem, who, for a considerable time, had been a pupil of the great astronomer Tycho Brahe, whom he zealously followed, constructing many instruments for the advancement of astronomical studies, for the promotion of the art of navigation, and of other sciences of like character, an interest in all of which he revived and furthered while at the same time he made new discoveries, as has become widely known from the publications which have issued from this printing house.' "

Blaeu may almost be considered by us the great-grandfather of the Ordnance survey and the modern Ordnance map, for, 100 years before Cassini and 150 years before General Roy laid out his triangulation base on Hounslow Heath, he undertook the exact measurement of a degree on the surface of the earth, anticipating the mathematician Snellius, who has usually been given the credit for the new method of map-construction based on triangulation. Blaeu measured the coast of the Netherlands from the mouth of the Meuse to the Texel, and it is said his error was only 66 metres, while the error of Snellius, over the same distance, was 3880 metres. It is not known why Blaeu did not publish his results.

He began his career by making globes, about which we shall have something to say in a moment. In 1605 he brought out a world map, which was so good that it was copied by Jodocus Hondius, who was the father-in-law of Jansson, head of the great rival firm to that of Blaeu. Although the taking of information from other people's maps was an accepted practice, Hondius and Jansson seem to have gone farther, for in 1608 Blaeu complained to the States of Holland and West Friesland, saying his business was being ruined because of copying of his work, and Hondius' world map of 1611 was very similar to Blaeu's.

His first Atlas was called an appendix to those of Mercator and Ortelius, but among the 103 maps in the book were many of his own. (Not all his maps have either his name or a date ; he also signed himself Alcmar, after his birthplace, or Caesius, the Latinised form of his name.)

In 1662 there appeared in eleven volumes the *Atlas Major*, into which the Blaeus had collected maps previously published, as well as many new ones. This was probably the greatest Atlas produced by the Dutch map-makers in the seventeenth century, and rivals those of Mercator and Ortelius. Latin, Dutch, French, and Spanish editions appeared, and it is not difficult for the collector to buy one of

he less well-known maps from this lovely Atlas to remind him
of the famous Dutchman. Many special editions, with the
maps beautifully coloured by hand and in expensive bindings,
were made ; it is said that a copy done for the occasion was
given to Admiral de Ruyter after his two-day battle with the
English in 1666, and one bound in royal purple was presented
to Sultan Mahommed IV of Turkey. The Sultan liked it so
much that he ordered the work to be translated into Turkish.
Volume 6 contains beautiful English county maps, and
Volume 5 those of Scotland. The maps in the English volume,
which was issued first in 1645, were based on those of John
Speed.

On the night of February 22nd, 1672, the Blaeus' printing-
house was burnt down and most of the plates destroyed.
Soon afterwards the firm seems to have gone out of business.

The rival firm of Jansson brought out a five-volume Atlas
in 1652, with fifty-six maps of the British Isles which, like
Blaeu's, were based on Saxton, with the text of Camden.

With these names ended the Dutch school of cartographers,
who, with the Englishmen and the Frenchmen, made possible
our modern maps. The Englishmen we shall read of in the
next chapter, but before passing on to the Frenchmen, a few
words on globes may be of interest.

The globes that one sees nowadays in classroom or at home,
and which are so useful to convey the real shape of the continents and the seaways that connect them, are descendants of
old instruments which were once of great importance. No
seaman of the time of the elder Blaeu would have sailed from
port for a voyage across the Atlantic without a globe of the
world to help him plot his course, and one of the sky to help
him identify the stars and so make sure of his position.

The oldest known terrestrial globe (one of the earth, as a
celestial globe is one of the sky) was made by Martin Behaim
of Nuremberg in the year that Columbus made his voyage.
It was a ball that had first been covered with strips of parch-
ment, and upon these had been drawn and coloured a map of
the world.

Later on globes were made of copper and then engraved,
or of wood, or of composition upon which an engraved or
hand-drawn map was pasted. It was early in the sixteenth
century when globe-makers learned to draw their maps on

gores, or strips of paper like two triangles joined base to base
so that they came to points at the two poles and were thickest
at the equator. When carefully done, and when the paper
had been stretched in places to take the curve of the sphere, a
set of these gores would exactly cover the globe : Mercator
who produced a famous globe in 1541, improved the work of
those who had gone before, and made the method practical.
Copies of both Mercator's terrestrial and celestial globes are
still in existence.

Hondius made globes, and it is not surprising that Blaeu
who had been taught instrument-making by Tycho Brahe
should have started his career by bringing out a globe 34 centi-
metres in diameter, in 1599, on the lines of Mercator's. This
had twelve gores, with the points which met at the poles pasted
over with circles of paper. The meridians and parallels are
marked in at intervals of 10°. About sixty of Blaeu's globes
still exist to-day. The increasing accuracy of maps and charts
and the greater knowledge of projections that followed
Mercator, led to there being less need for globes as instruments of navigation.

The first French Atlas, the *Théâtre François*, was published
in 1594, and is very rare ; it contained maps that were mostly
copied from Ortelius and Mercator by a Fleming, Gabriel
Tavernier. Many reprints of it exist. The line of famous
French cartographers begins about 1650, at almost the same
date as the Dutch line came to an end (about 1670). The best
known names are the Sansons and the Cassinis, both of whom
are also associated with projections, the English Ordnance
Survey being made on the Cassini projection.

The maps of Nicolas Sanson, and his sons Nicolas, Adrien
and Guillaume, engraved and published for 100 years after
1650, are often to be met with : lovely some of them are, with
little outlines of churches and buildings in different sizes to
show towns of varying importance, and their highly ornamented *cartouches*, the panels in which were put the name of
the map, the scale, and other particulars. These *cartouches*
tended to collect all the decoration which in the earlier Dutch
maps had been scattered over the surface. England and
Wales are covered in five specially well-engraved maps in
Sanson's Atlas, *Cartes Générales de toutes les Parties du
Monde*, 1658, which were probably based on the Quarter

master's map that Hollar made for use in the Civil War (see page 102).

The scales in the *cartouches* tended sometimes to be complicated affairs. Each country of Europe, and in some cases each province, had its own unit of measurement. All French provinces before the Revolution had a greater and a lesser league, and some a middle league as well. On one of the sheets of Julien's map of France in 1751 there are twenty different scales shown.

At the end of the Sanson period, from 1750 to the French Revolution, come the two Cassinis, César François Cassini de Thury and his son Jacques Dominique. They worked out and applied to the mapping of France the system of triangulation which had been foreshadowed by Blaeu and improved by Snellius, and which was adopted from them by our own Ordnance Survey. Over a period of 45 years they mapped the whole of France, on a scale of $\frac{1}{86,400}$, against our one-inch with its scale of $\frac{1}{63,360}$, in 180 sheets, a reduction to twenty-four sheets being published by Louis Capitaine in 1789.

The work of the Cassinis, like our own Survey, had its origin in military needs. The elder Cassini attended Louis XV as cartographer and military engineer, and wrote a book about it, during the campaigns in Flanders and Central Europe between 1745 and 1748. As a result of his work in the field, Cassini was ordered to map the whole of France at the Government's expense ; but it seems that as the French finances got worse, so the subsidy diminished, and the Cassinis finished the task with their own money.

Maps by two other Frenchmen are often seen, and are worth collecting and studying, and so are mentioned here. The *Atlas Universel* (1757), of the two Robert de Vaugondys, and the *Atlas Geographique et Militaire de la France* (1751), of R. J. Julien.

Whereas the series of English county maps can be traced from those of Saxton right to the present day, the maps of the French provinces to which they correspond stop sharply with the French Revolution, when the old provincial boundaries were abolished, and uninteresting maps of the new departments into which France was divided appeared.

G

CHAPTER NINE

THE OLD MAPS OF THE BRITISH ISLES

England and Wales. In the windows of second-hand book
shops, perhaps framed or perhaps fastened to the window itself
with little strips of adhesive paper, can often be seen old maps
of Great Britain or of the English counties, while inside the
bookseller will show to the enquirer his full stocks. They look
curious and full of interest to the passer-by, with their
hummocky hills, old-fashioned writing, queer spelling of
place-names, dragons and fish playing in the sea ; all of which
tell him of an earlier practice in making maps.

There are in existence one or two manuscript maps of Great
Britain, such as those made by the monk of St. Albans,
Matthew Paris, about 1250, and the one in the Bodleian Library
at Oxford, which dates from 1300, and very early and rare
printed maps of the British Isles such as those by Lily and
Humphrey Lluyd, which were produced on the Continent.
The first English cartographer, however, whose maps became
widespread and well known is Christopher Saxton, who was
born about 1542 and died about 1611. His birthplace was the
little hamlet of Dunningley in Yorkshire, and he must have
been proud of it, for the name appears not only on his York
shire map of 1577, but later on his general map of England
and Wales.

In 1570 Saxton began a survey of England and Wales, and
he covered the whole country in nine years. It seems that his
expenses and salary were paid by his patron, Thomas Seckford,
Master of Requests and of the Court of Wards ; but he
reaped a fuller reward not from the sale of his maps, but by
grants of land and offices from Queen Elizabeth. For instance
in 1573 there is recorded a grant of the manor of Grigston, in
Suffolk, " for certain good causes grand charges & expense
lately had and sustained in the survey of divers parts of
England ". The manor was to be held by Saxton and his
successors for twenty-one years at a rental of £10 5s. 11d.
Later he was given the office of collector of rents of all the
manors and lands that used to belong to the Priory and Hos
pital of St. John of Jerusalem.

That his countrymen had great hopes of his work may be

een by this quotation from William Harrison's *Description of Britaine* in the 1577 edition of Holinshed's *Chronicles*, the ook from which Shakespeare learned much of his history :

" . . . a friende of myne, by whose traveyle and hys maisters xcessive charges I doubt not, but my country men eare long hall see all Englande set foorth in severall shyres after the naner that Ortelius hath dealt other countries of the mayne mainland, as in Spanish Main), to the great benefite of our ation and everlasting fame of the aforesayde parties."

We can only admire a man who performed such a huge task o well, for his maps, an exclusive licence to sell which was iven him for ten years from 1577, were so good that his work was the basis for most of the work done before Cary, that is, for ver 200 years. Letters were written to influential people to elp him in his work, and it was requested that in Wales " the aid Justices shalbe aiding and assisting unto him to see him onducted unto any towre Castle highe place or hill to view hat countrey and that he may be accompanied wth ij or iij onest men such as do best know the cuntrey for the better ccomplishement of that service and that at his depture from ny towne or place that he hath taken the view of the said owne do set forth a horseman that can speke both Welche nd Englishe to safe conduct him to the next market owne. . . ."

These county maps of England and Wales were printed rom copper plates, and the scale to which they were made aries, Hampshire, for instance, being about 1 inch to 3¾ niles. The length of Saxton's mile varies from map to map, he average being 10½ furlongs to the mile. The mile that was sed by these early map-makers was usually the old British nile, which was the pre-Roman Gallic league of 2428 yards. he first to use the present standard mile of 1760 yards was)gilby, in his road-book *Britannia*, in 1675 (see page 107).

His Atlas contained thirty-five maps, engraved between 574 and 1578. Saxton's Atlas was issued with an elaborate rontispiece showing Queen Elizabeth in the centre, sitting nder a canopy bearing the royal arms and two cupids, olding laurel crowns. On each side are men with globes and ompasses. This Atlas was many times reprinted, and the naps altered in date and details.

Saxton's maps were mostly engraved by Dutch artists,

20704

though five county maps and the frontispiece were done by
Englishmen. As an example of Saxton's work let us take the
map of Cornwall, reproduced as Plate 16 in Humphreys' *Old
Decorative Maps and Charts*. The first thing that strikes
us is that the county is not quite the right shape as we are
accustomed to know it from modern maps ; we notice the
ornamental borders, and that the county is described as
" *Promontorium hoc in mare proiectum Cornubia dicitur.*"
(This promontory projecting into the sea is called Cornwall.
The map is dated : *Factum est hoc opus An Dm* 1576 *et D
Elizabethe Reginae* 18 (This work was done in the Year of the
Lord 1576 and of Queen Elizabeth 18). Over the county
name is the royal arms, surrounded by pictures of sea
monsters, tridents, shells, and seaweed, whilst ships and
dragons are scattered over the sea. We find Saxton's name
as *Christopherus Saxton descripsit*, and the engraver a
LENAERT TERWOORT ANTVER PLANUS SCULPSIT
(Lanaert Terwoort engraved the plate at Antwerp). The
map shows rivers, hills, bridges (but no roads), and hundreds
A hundred, which is found marked on all early maps
down to Morden's time and later, was originally supposed to
contain a hundred families, but later became an administrative unit.

We may be particularly proud of Saxton, for he was the first
in any country to undertake such a detailed survey, or to
publish maps based upon it that were so good. The French
collection of provincial maps, the *Théâtre François*, published
nearly twenty years after Saxton's Atlas, was much inferior
We still do not know how Saxton carried out the survey, or
what instruments were used to fix points and measure
distances. A series of reproductions of Saxton's maps are
produced cheaply in colour and sold by the British Museum

In 1577 the Dutch map-maker, Ortelius, visited England
and met the historian Camden, and succeeded in persuading
him to write his county history of England, *Britannia*. The
1607 edition of this most famous of all county histories carried
maps engraved by William Kip and William Hole, based on
the work of Saxton and Norden, but reduced in size, and these
are very often seen in shops from one or other of the editions
of *Britannia*. Petrus Kaerius, whom we remember in connection with Mercator, issued the maps in a pocket size in

Dutch edition of Camden in 1617 (though some of the maps are dated 1599) and in later English editions.

Norden was a contemporary of Saxton who produced engraved maps of Middlesex and Hertfordshire, and surveyed Essex, Surrey, Sussex, Cornwall, Northants, Hampshire, and possibly Kent ; his maps have much the same appearance as those of Saxton, but they show the roads. Norden did not get support for his scheme for a complete series of county histories, each of which was to be accompanied by a map, and he died in poverty. He also invented the triangular table of distances, which we use nowadays for so many purposes.

It was upon the work of these two map-makers that John Speed based his maps. Speed was born in 1552 at Farndon in Cheshire ; he followed his father's profession of a tailor, and was also admitted to the freedom of the Merchant Taylors Company. He married and lived at Moorfields, and it was the interest that he took in antiquities that brought him to the notice of Sir Fulke Greville, who gave him an income so that he could devote his whole time to research and map-making. Speed writes of his patron, " whose merits to me I do acknowledge in setting this hand free from the daily imployment of a manuall trade and giving it full liberty thus to express the inclination of my mind, himself being the procurer of my present estate ". Speed's maps also owed much to the Dutchmen, as, indeed, do all the maps of the period. He was not a great map-maker, but he made them popular, ornamented them more highly, and sold ten maps for every one of Saxton's.

Speed's *Theatre of the Empire of Great Britaine*, published in 1611, contained a complete set of English and Welsh county maps, together with a printed description on the back of each map. More decoration is evident than with Saxton, and round the maps are coats of arms, small town plans, or pictures of famous places in each county. A short description of two Speed maps, of Surrey and Middlesex, will make this clear.

The Surrey map is titled " Surrey described and divided into Hundreds ", and shows in the left top corner a picture of Richmont (Richmond Palace), in the right top corner Nonsuch (Nonsuch House). Down each side are the arms of various Earls of Surrey, while at the bottom is the scale and the following legends : " Described by the travills of John

Norden.   Augmented and performed by Iohn Speede".
" Jodocus Hondius caelavit.   Anno 1610."

That of Middlesex is headed " Middle-sex described with
the most famous Cities of London and Westminster ".   In
the four corners are plans of London and Westminster, and
drawings of Saint Peter's (Westminster Abbey) and Saint
Paul's.   At the bottom we have " Described by Iohn Norden.
Augmented by I. Speed.   Solde in Popes head alley against
the Exchange by George Humble ".   At the sides are two
open books ; on the pages of the left-hand one is a description
of the Abbey and Saint Paul's ; on the right : " The large
circuite, wth multitude of streetes besydes the beautifull &
stately buildings in this fayre, and most famous Citie
LONDON :   can no wise be demonstrated in soe litle
compase, as here I am inforced to shewe.   But as Hercules
his bodye might be measured by his 1 foote, and the universall
Globe drawe in a smale circle :   Soe in this, rather conceit the
magnificens thereof in mȳde, then curiously seeke satisfaction
by the sight :   whose pleasant situation, beautye, and rich
blessings both for soyll and sea equals (yf not exceeds) any
Citie under Heaven.   The trew plott whereof I purposely
reserve to a further leasure & larger Scale."

In the reign of Charles II, Moses Pitt conceived the ambitious design of mapping the whole of the then known world,
on an English basis, to compete with (and surpass) the atlases
of Blaeu and other foreigners.   The printing was entrusted to
the Clarendon Press at Oxford, and the result was a truly
magnificent example of the printer's art.   Unfortunately,
Pitt's money ran out and he was cast into the debtor's prison
when only four of the projected twelve volumes had been
published.

Another seventeenth-century cartographer of interest was
Hollar, famous for his prints.   He produced from Saxton's
map of England and Wales (an original of which is not known,
but which made appearances in altered forms until 1720) a
map in six sheets which covered England and Wales.   This
was made to fold for the pocket, and although it did not show
the roads, it was this map, known as the Quartermaster's Map,
that was used by the armies in the Civil War.

Richard Blome's maps are often seen, from the *Britannia*
compiled by the author, and they are very distinctive.   Blome

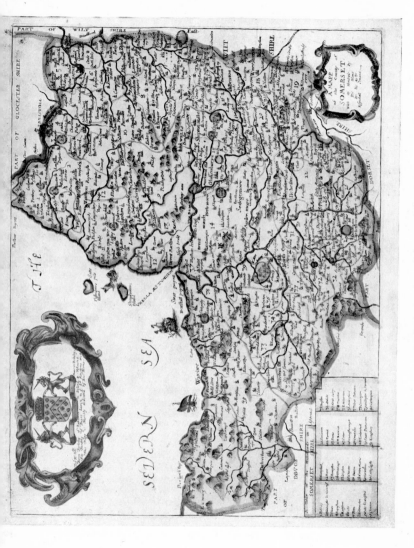

RICHARD BLOME'S MAP OF SOMERSET.

was a heraldic painter, and did work pleasant to look at, but it was largely derived from Speed, as his book was adapted from Camden's book of the same name.

Towards the end of the century a new group of map-makers arose. Of their productions the commonest are the maps of John Morden, which appeared in the 1695 edition of Camden's *Britannia*. There is a map for every English county, but instead of a separate one for each county of Wales, the Morden maps cover North and South Wales on one sheet each. A collector will probably start off with a Morden map, for one of his, uncoloured, of most of the counties, can be bought for two or three shillings.

The preface to this edition of Camden says : " The maps are all newly engrav'd, either according to Surveys never before publish'd, or according to such as have been made and printed since Saxton and Speed. Where actual Surveys could be had, they were purchas'd at any rate ; and for the rest, one of the best copies extant was sent to some of the most knowing Gentlemen in each County, with a request to supply the defects, rectifie the positions, and correct the false spellings. And that nothing might be wanting to render them as com-plete and accurate as might be, this whole business was com-mitted to Mr. Robert Morden, a person of known abilities in these matters, who took care to revise them, to see the slips of the Engraver mended, and the corrections, return'd out of the several Counties, duly inserted. Upon the whole, we need not scruple to affirm, that they are by much the fairest and most correct of any that have yet appear'd."

Morden began business in London as a map- and globe-maker in 1668. He published many geographical works besides his maps.

Subsequent to the Morden series, the eighteenth-century cartographers became more ambitious, and a number of elaborate large-scale maps of individual counties were pro-duced, which were financed by the wealthier residents of the counties concerned, and encouraged by the Society of Arts, which in 1759 and subsequent years announced that : " The Society proposes to give a Sum not exceeding 100L as a Gratuity to any Person or Persons, who shall make an accurate actual Survey of any County . . . and if any Person or Persons do propose to make such Survey, they are desired to signify their particular Intentions, on or before the second Tuesday in November next, that the Society may not engage in greater Expences than shall be found convenient." The first premium was paid for a map of Devon by Mr. Benjamin Donn.

An example is John Rocque's map of Surrey, published in 1762, which was on the large scale of 2 inches to the mile. Sir C. Close says " . . . every house is shown ; every road, stream, garden, park and wood. It is a complete and elaborate map ; one could count the number of houses and almost calculate the number of the inhabitants. The only weak feature of the map is the hachuring—that is, vertical shading— of the hills ; the style is no doubt derived from contemporary French maps, in which the hachuring gives the impression of a flat plateau cut up by deep water-courses, or flat-topped hills standing on a plain. But it is a splendid map, and has been reproduced on a smaller scale by the Surrey Archaeological Society."

Another is a 2-inch-to-the-mile map of Sussex, brought out in 1796, and estimated in the prospectus to cost £2400, for surveying, printing, and engraving, 400 subscribers at six guineas each being asked for.

County maps by the Bowens and Kitchen are often found, produced about 1770, and can be bought cheaply. These contain much description and history, both on the face of the map and in the margins, as for instance : " Ware, 20 miles from London ; Great quantities of Malt and Corn are sent to London from this Town Weekly in Barges by the River Lee. At Amwell within a mile of this Town, is the Source of the New River, which supplies London and great part of Westminster with Water." (From the *Atlas Anglicanus*, or a Complete Sett of Maps of the Counties of South Britain, of Eman : Bowen.)

So we come to John Cary, who was born in 1754, and died in 1835, and to his relations who worked with him. His most famous work was his *New Map*, published in eighty-one sheets in 1794, but county maps, printed in colour for the first time, and in several different sizes, will be found by him.

Cary's drawing and engraving were greatly in advance of the map-makers who went before him, like Kitchen and the Bowens, and of some who came after, and his work compares favourably with that of the Ordnance maps which

WESTMINSTER

SAINT PETERS

PART OF

Kings Langley
Langley Abbey
Abbam
Shenly

SHIRE
Bushy Heath Watford
Bushy

GOARE H
Canons
Grt. Stanmor
Pinner
Woodhall
Kenton
Wembl

Chalfont
Breakspeares
Harefeild
Marshall
Brohamborowe
Nethall Ledge
Vxbridge
Ichenham
Ruislip
Ickenham
Swakleys
Hillesden
Greneford
Northolt
PART OF
REITHORNE HUND
Earls Hillingdon
Perivale
Dawley
Cowley
Hayes
Northill
Syon
Drayton Well
Southoll
Norwode
Morden
Harlington
Greneford Parke
West Bedfont
Bedfont
Belers
ISTL
Hefton
Hounslow
Heston
BUCKINGHAM

Colnebrok
Stanwell

SHIRE
Eaton
Batchet
Ditton
Bulney ferrie
Stanburh
STANES
Ashford
Felham
Littleton
SPELL
HORNE HUN
Windfore
Egham
Chertsey
Lalam
Sheperton
PART OF
BERKSHIRE

Windelore
Parke
Egham
Thorpe
Manford
Shepperton
Walton

Jodocus Hondius celavit
Otlandes

were beginning to appear at the same time. They have a very modern appearance, as can be seen by comparing a Cary map, on the one hand, with a Morden of 100 years before, and on the other with an Ordnance map of the present day, over 100 years later.

There are three sets of county maps of England and Wales. The first, very small maps about the size of the pages of this book, was called *The Traveller's Companion*, and first appeared in 1790. Then the *New and Correct English Atlas*, first published in 1787, in larger size, and lastly the *New English Atlas*, with still larger maps. These are in addition to the county maps used in the new edition of Camden's *Britannia* that was brought out in 1789 in four volumes.

The collector will find it easy to get a specimen of Cary's county maps, and he will also often come across some of his other work—for instance, a road-book, a foreign map, or the plan of a canal or road.

After Cary county maps become less interesting to the eye, and one becomes more concerned with the early productions of the Ordnance Survey, but one must make an exception of the lovely Greenwood maps produced round about 1830, and which show the beginnings of the railway system side by side with the old horse-drawn railways such as existed in the Northumberland coalfields, and with the canal system which reached the peak of its development at that time. These were reductions from the big Greenwood series, on the scale of 1 inch to the mile, and based on a survey begun in 1814. Each county was covered in four or six sheets, priced usually at three guineas each. The plan was never completed, ending soon after 1830, when Bucks, Cambs, Herefordshire, Herts, Norfolk, and Oxfordshire still remained to complete the series.

Many of the smaller maps, such as those by Moule which have vignettes of famous places in the county concerned, are attractive when they are coloured.

The collecting of county maps, especially of the county in which one lives, has great interest, for one can trace on the faces of the maps changes in boundaries, alterations in the spelling of place-names, the filling in of roads, canals, and railways, and the growth of detail in the map as it approaches modern times. Apart from the well-known maps, some of which we have mentioned in this chapter, there are many

small and cheap ones which, by hunting in the second-hand
bookshops, you will be able to buy cheaply. For such a
collection you should consult *The Printed Maps in the Atlases
of Great Britain and Ireland*, by T. Chubb, for in it you will
be able to identify the maps you see and find out their dates
and particulars about them. For about a dozen counties
there are books listing the maps of that county, with detailed
descriptions, and if you collect one of these, it would be wise
to get a copy of the book that deals with it.

The price of old maps varies very much from county to
county, for most are bought for purely decorative reasons, and
so the counties round London, where there is a large well-to-do
population within easy reach of the London bookshops, are
especially scarce, Sussex most of all. If your interest, then, is
topographical—that is, in some particular area where you live
and work—you must be prepared to limit your collection if you
live in the Home Counties to exclude maps that are beyond
your pocket. The smaller maps can still be found for a little
money and much patience.

If, however, you are interested in cartography, and want to
form a collection with perhaps one map of each of the more
important cartographers, then you can buy the cheaper maps
of the great map-makers ; for instance, Speed maps of
Rutland and Huntingdon, or of most of the Welsh counties,
can be bought for a fraction of the price of a Sussex, Kent,
Berkshire, or Cornwall.

A collection of county maps might end with the Greenwoods,
and after that you would include specimens of the various
editions of the Ordnance maps and of the 6-inch and 25-inch
plans ; and so would be completed a history of mapping over
350 years.

If, as is more than likely, you cannot afford any money for
a collection, you will get a great deal of interest from the books
listed on page 138. There are many illustrations, and once you
have fixed in your mind the look of a Saxton or a Speed or a
Blome, you will be able to go to museum or bookshop and
recognise the work of these map-makers.

Many old maps are found coloured. The engraving as it
came off the copper-plate was in black on white, and the
colouring was then added by hand, or the map left uncoloured.
A great many have been coloured in modern times, and if this

has been well done it is not easy to tell the age of the colouring. Therefore do not pay more attention to, or money for, the colouring than is necessary to make sure that it has been well done and gives a pleasing result. Cary's maps were the first to be printed in colour, and after comparison you will easily be able to distinguish colour-printing from water-colour.

The number of British county maps can be guessed at from figures given by Sir George Fordham. He knows of 155 separate plates that have produced county maps of Hertfordshire ; of these there have been 327 re-impressions, making 482 different specimens. Multiply this by the number of counties in England and Wales, add the general maps, and those of railways, roads, and canals, and one has some idea of the many that exist.

An interesting by-product of the study of maps is to learn a little of the early road-books and road-maps, for they show very graphically the growth of the roads, as a result of the demands of commerce, travel, and the Post Office. There is a detailed article on the subject in Sir George Fordham's *Studies in Carto-Bibliography*.

The only early maps of England that showed the roads were the two county maps of Middlesex and Hertfordshire, published by Norden, though we have mentioned his triangular distance tables, forty of which were published in 1625 in a little book called *England : An Intended Guyde, for English Travailers*.

It was in 1675 that John Ogilby brought out his *Britannia, or, an Illustration of the Kingdom of England and Dominion of Wales* ; By a Geographical and Historical Description of the Principal Roads thereof Actually Admeasured and Delineated in a Century of Whole-Sheet Copper-Sculps. . . . By John Ogilby, His Majesty's Cosmographer, and Master of His Majesty's Revels in the Kingdom of Ireland.

The chief roads of England and Wales were engraved on strips lying side by side, showing the road and the towns and villages on its course, and the distance at each mile from the starting point, there being altogether 100 folio plates and 200 pages of text. Ogilby actually measured the roads with a measuring-wheel, and a huge task it must have been, for he said later that it had cost £7,000 to make the survey and to publish the book. Two other road-books were derived from Ogilby's work, and both will be found of interest.

An atlas appeared in 1719, in which John Senex re-issued with corrections Ogilby's plates in a reduced size, and this went through several editions.

More or less at the same time came out a book that the collector may find without much difficulty, the *Britannia Depicta*, a book of 273 plates, consisting of road-strips three or four to a page, with text, county maps, and coats-of-arms as well.

From Morden onwards the county maps began to show the roads, first sketchily, and then in more detail. Cary's maps give them accurately, but in addition to the maps that he published, he brought out in 1798 his *New Itinerary*, which resulted from an agreement he made to measure exactly the post and mail-coach roads in exchange for the right exclusively to publish the results. Under this agreement 9000 miles of roads were measured. The book as originally issued consisted of distance tables and notes on the country passed through, and a few maps, but in later editions more of the latter were brought in to illustrate the journeys.

These are only a few of the many road-maps that were published from the days of Ogilby up to the middle of the nineteenth century, when the roads almost ceased to be used as the railways took the coaching and industrial traffic from them, and these are in truth the ancestors of our present motoring and cycling maps. Apart from the road-strips and road-maps, there are many books of distances and description which are well worth looking for, both for their own sakes and to see what the author had to say 100 or 200 years ago about any special part of the country that we know well.

Scotland. Compared with the long range of the county maps of England, Scotland and Ireland make a poor showing; at the same time, those maps that exist are of great interest, though, owing to their greater scarcity, they are not often seen and have seldom been written about.

On Ptolemy's map Scotland was shown as bending sharply to the east, so that all the country north of the Forth and Clyde is lying at right angles to England. Ruysch, whom we have mentioned before as an early improver on Ptolemy, corrected this error in 1508, though it had already been corrected in

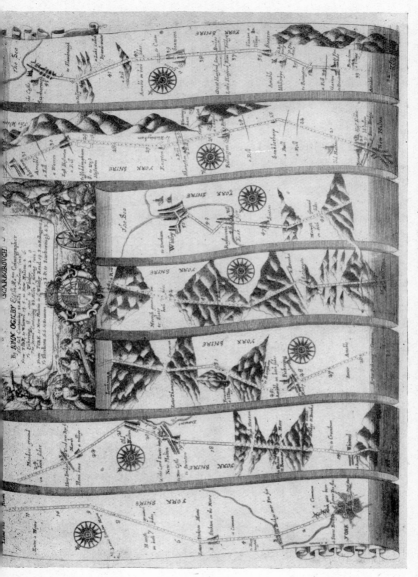

A SHEET OF IOHN OGILVY'S ROAD-STRIPS.

some of the portolan charts produced by the Mediterranean chart-makers. It is curious, however, that in spite of Ptolemy and Ruysch, later minor map-makers of Italy and France showed Scotland as an island as late as 1544, following the "monkish" maps of the British Isles.

The work of Mercator and Ortelius was a great improvement upon these, and provided the base for Speed's map of Scotland; but it was to Nicolay d'Arfeville, who in 1583 brought out a map based on a voyage made in 1540 by King James V of Scotland and described by his pilot, Alexander Lyndsay, that we owe the first detailed description of the Scottish coastline, and to Timothy Pont that we are indebted for the first survey of the interior.

The first Atlas of Scottish maps was published in 1654 by Blaeu as Volume 5 of his *New Atlas*. The title-page, which is illustrated by Chubb, shows the arms of Scotland supported by two unicorns, one holding the lion flag and the other the St. Andrew's Cross, with the motto *In Defence* above. Beneath the arms, and between two pillars, is the title: *Guil. et Joannis Blaeu Theatrum Orbis Terrarum, sive Atlas Novus. Pars Quinta.* Beneath: *Amstelodami apud Ionnem Blaeu, M.DC.LIV.*

There are forty-nine maps in this volume, one of Great Britain according to Ptolemy, two of Scotland, and the rest sectional maps. Most of them had been drawn by Timothy Pont, who in 1600 had been appointed minister of the parish of Dunnett in Caithness, in the north of Scotland. He was not, perhaps, a very conscientious minister, for he must have spent long periods away from his parish, but he was an enthusiastic map-maker. He surveyed nearly all of Scotland, and one can hardly imagine how difficult a task it must have been, with the country undrained, unfenced, and almost without roads as it was then. When Pont died about 1612, his maps were bought by Sir John Scot of Scotstarvet. At the request of King Charles I Sir Robert Gordon of Straloch continued them, and added some of his own to make the series complete, and then in 1645 Sir John Scot took them to Amsterdam, where they were engraved and incorporated into Blaeu's *Atlas*. Two titles of the sectional maps will show that they were not true county maps, but covered districts individual to the *Atlas*:

16. PRAEFECTURA KIRCUBRIENSIS, quae Gallo-
vidia maxime orientalis est.   The Stuartrie of Kircubright,
The most easterlie part of Galloway. Auct. Tim. Pont.

17. CARRICTA MERIDIONALIS.   The South Part of
Carrick. Auct. Tim. Pont.

It was not until 1725 that Herman Moll, a cartographer
who also produced a set of English county maps, brought out
a set for Scotland. It was titled : *A Set of Thirty New and
Correct Maps of Scotland Divided into Shires, &c. A Work
long wanted, and very useful for all Gentlemen that Travel to
any part of that Kingdom. All, except Two, composed and done
by Herman Moll, Geographer.*

The maps were smaller than those of Blaeu, and were
based on the shires into which Scotland had been divided.
The Atlas was reprinted in 1896.

This was followed by a collection of thirty-three smaller
maps on the Edinburgh meridian, by Thomas Kitchen, in
1749. This was titled : *Geographia Scotiae : being new and
correct Maps of all the Counties and Islands in the Kingdom of
Scotland. Containing the Universities, Cities, Presbytery, and
Market-Towns, Rivers, Locks, Roads, &c. With General Map
of the whole Kingdom, from the latest Observations.*

This was followed in 1776 by a road-book done by George
Taylor and Andrew Skinner, with 61 plates of the roads, and
then by another Atlas, by Mostyn John Armstrong, called :
*A Scotch Atlas ; or Description of the Kingdom of Scotland :
divided into counties, with the subdivisions of Sherifdoms ;
shewing their respective boundaries and extent, soil, produce,
mines, minerals, metals, their trade and manufactures ; also
their Cities, Chief Towns, Seaports, Mountains, Rivers, Forests,
Locks, &c. with the Principal Great and Bye Roads, Passes,
Forts and other Particulars. The Whole taken from Topographical Surveys, regulated by Astronomical Observations.*

Beneath the title is a picture showing a factory, with arms
and ammunition piled in the foreground, while a man wheels
cannon-balls on a truck, and the arms of Scotland.

Other series, listed in Chubb, appeared during the nineteenth century, and those who are interested in Scottish maps
should consult Shearer's book, *Old Maps and Map-Makers of
Scotland.*

Ireland. The maps of Ireland which had appeared in early atlases had been general maps ; it was left to Sir William Petty in 1685 to issue the first atlas with Irish provincial and county maps. In this there is a general map of Ireland, four provincial maps, and the rest those of the counties. The volume is titled : *Hiberniae Delineatio quoad hactenus licuit Perfectissima Studio Guilielmi Petty Eq^{tis} Aurati.* In the same year what was called *A Geographicall Description of ye Kingdom of Ireland. Collected from ye actual Survey made by Sr William Petty Corrected and amended . . .* was brought out, with reduced copies of Petty's maps. There was another edition of Petty in 1720. Apart from Taylor and Skinner's road-maps of Ireland on the same lines as those for Scotland, the only other Atlas which appeared before the nineteenth century that the collector is likely to see is one by an Irish cartographer, Bernard Scalé, published in 1776 : *An Hibernian Atlas ; or General Description of the Kingdom of Ireland : Divided into Provinces ; with its sub-divisions of Counties, Baronies, &c. Shewing their boundaries, extent, soil, produce, contents, measure, Members of Parliament and number of inhabitants ; also the Cities, Boroughs, Villages, Mountains, Bogs, Lakes, Rivers, and Natural Curiosities. Together with the Great and Bye Post Roads. The whole taken from actual Surveys and Observations. By Bernard Scalé, Land Surveyor, and beautifully engraved on 78 copper plates, by Messrs. Ellis and Palmer. . . .*

CHAPTER TEN

THE ORDNANCE MAPS AND PLANS

IT is not easy for us to realise that two hundred years ago no
maps of Britain in detail existed, and that travellers, soldiers,
and the Government had to rely upon the productions which
we have been considering in the preceding chapter, and upon
a few special sketches and surveys made for particular
purposes.

One of the most urgent reasons for requiring an accurate
map is in order to make war, and the Ordnance Survey may
be traced back for its beginning to the last Jacobite armed
effort, when Prince Charles Edward landed in Scotland, and,
at the head of a largely Highland army, marched as far south
as Derby, causing a panic in London that made the Bank of
England pay out in sixpences so as to delay those who wanted
to fly with their money or hide it ; then, concluding that
England was not going to support him, he retreated to
Scotland again, and was brought to battle and defeated by the
Duke of Cumberland at Culloden in April 1746.

After this rising had been put down, General Wade was
ordered to open up the Highlands by building a system of
military roads, which would allow troops to be moved rapidly
about the country in the event of more Jacobite movements
on the same principle that the Romans had adopted in their
occupied countries. The task of mapping, which had to go
on parallel with the road-building if future battles were to be
won, was given to an assistant of Cumberland's, Colonel
Watson. The work was begun in 1747, and the principal
name connected with it is that of William Roy, in that year a
man of twenty-one. The maps were made, and they are now
in the British Museum—the first to be made by the military
authorities for the Government.

Map-making was interrupted by the Seven Years' War, but
as Roy wrote later, " On the conclusion of the peace of 1763
it came for the first time under the consideration of Government, to make a general survey of the whole island at the public
cost. Towards the execution of this work, whereof the
direction was to have been committed to my charge, the map
of Scotland was to be made subservient."

A little later, in 1765, the first link was made between the Honourable Board of Ordnance and the map-making idea, when Roy was given the post of Surveyor-General of Coasts and Engineer for making Military Surveys under the Board. This body, which dates from the fifteenth century, lasted till 1857, and its name still survives in the Royal Army Ordnance Corps.

However, before much could be done, another war, that of American Independence, interfered, and money was tight and soldiers busy. It was not till after the peace of 1783 that the next step was taken, and the initiative for it came from outside. Cassini, of whom we know, suggested that for the purpose of checking certain astronomical calculations it would be valuable to work out the exact distance between the Royal Observatories at London and Paris. The two Governments agreed to carry out the work, and the English operations were put in charge of Roy, who constructed the base line for his great triangle on Hounslow Heath, and carried out the work with the aid of a theodolite specially made for him by a famous instrument-maker of the time, Jesse Ramsden.

Roy died in 1790, and with him ended the period in which the mapping of Britain had been thought of, hoped for, and experiments to that end carried out. In the next year the Duke of Richmond, Master-General of His Majesty's Ordnance, had the Trigonometrical Survey constituted. The principal reason why the matter was taken up at this time was perhaps the outbreak of the French Revolution two years before, and the probability in the minds of the Army leaders of 1791 that before long England would be at war with France.

The offices of the Survey were established with those of the Ordnance in the Tower of London, and work began. Given the military reasons for the mapping, it was natural that the first maps should be those of the south of England, and under the Directorship of Colonel William Mudge, one of the best-known names in connection with Ordnance maps, the first map, *General Survey of England and Wales ; an Entirely New and Accurate Survey of the County of Kent, with Part of the County of Essex*, was published on the first day of the nineteenth century, 1st January, 1801.

The first requirement for a national undertaking of this size was to find a body of efficient field-workers to carry out

H

the Survey, and of draughtsmen to draw the results ; and so
in 1805 the Corps of Royal Military Surveyors and Draughtsmen was brought into being—men who were trained by the
Ordnance Survey. The establishment of the Corps raised the
level of the work performed, for some of the early surveying
had been done by civil surveyors temporarily employed, and
was not up to Mudge's standard. The Corps was abolished
in 1817, but General Colby, a successor of Mudge, raised it
again in 1823, and the next year it became the 13th (Survey)
Company of the Royal Engineers.

This map of Kent, and its successors for many years, was
engraved on copper, like the maps of the last chapter. This
method of printing, which is obsolete now for most purposes
except such things as visiting-cards and letter-headings, was
very slow, twenty copies an hour being considered a good
speed, but it allowed very fine lines to be cut on the plate,
and so, when the cuts had been inked and the paper then
pressed into them, very finely printed lines were obtainable
on the final map. One can see this if one examines a copy of
such a map, and sees the fine hachuring, the thin parallel lines
indicating the hills. The map is a good deal simpler than our
present ones, because of the absence of the modern detail of
railways, inns, foot-paths, power-lines, and so on, and also
of contour lines, but it does not appear at all old-fashioned.
The printing was in black and white only. The scale was
1 inch to the mile, although most of the field work was
done at 2 inches to the mile and then reduced : there were,
however, small areas which were done at other scales before
reduction.

Essex, Surrey, and Sussex followed, and year after year the
work went on, till in 1844 the series had reached the Hull-
Preston line. Each map was considered, however, as a separate
problem, and six different meridians were used—those of
Dunnose, Clifton Beacon, Burleigh Moor, Delamere, Moel
Rhyddled, and Greenwich, and therefore there was no exact
correspondence between one map and the next. These surveying meridians, chosen to minimise distortion, must not be
confused with the Greenwich meridian, that line of longitude
which is now accepted throughout the world as the one from
which the others are constructed, and the time at all places on
the earth's surface calculated. We notice that one of the

meridians used by the Survey was the Greenwich meridian itself.

The choice of meridian has an interesting history, and it is only in our own day that world agreement has been gained for one rather than another. In the Middle Ages it was seen to be essential to have one meridian which would be generally accepted, so that all other lines of longitude could be measured off from it. With lines of latitude, the Equator was the obvious line, and there was no difficulty. The Ptolemaic tradition put this initial meridian through the Azores or the Canary Islands, which were as far west as the knowledge of that time extended. Saxton's large general map of England and Wales (about 1584) is drawn on the meridian of the island of St. Mary, the most easterly of the Azores Group. The navigator John Davis wrote in a pamphlet of 1594, called *The Seaman's Secrets*, that the best meridian ran through Saint Michael, also in the Azores, because he thought that at that place there was no variation, and the meridian ran through both the magnetic and the geographical pole. London on this meridian would be about $25° 54'$ E.

Mercator, following Ptolemy, chose the Canaries, and then changed to Corvo in the Azores. Ortelius, Jansson, and Blaeu used the Isla del Fuego in the Cape Verde Islands; Blaeu later proposed the peak of Teneriffe in the Canaries, and was followed by the Dutch. French ships were ordered by Richelieu in 1634 to calculate their meridians from Ferro (Hierro) in the Canaries, and this became the most usually accepted meridian till about 1800. Early Spanish and Portuguese map-makers had tried to put the meridian on the line of demarcation between the Spanish and Portuguese spheres of influence in the New World which the Pope had placed at 370 leagues (a league was three sea miles) west of the Cape Verde Islands.

English maps, after the appearance of John Seller's map of Hertfordshire in 1676, were drawn on a meridian of London, or, more accurately, St. Paul's Cathedral. Cary's *New Map of England and Wales*, 1794, was the first to use the meridian of Greenwich Observatory, this being due to the progress of the Ordnance Survey. Greenwich meridian was adopted for the Survey, and the others were used only for surveying purposes.

In the meantime, a new development had taken place. In 1824, a Select Committee of the House of Commons recommended a survey of Ireland on the basis of 6 inches to the mile, in order that the local finances could be reorganised, and said :

" Whilst your Committee express their belief that the execution of the survey cannot be placed in better hands than in those of the Ordnance Officers, they cannot but add, that it is expedient to give much greater dispatch to this work than what has occurred in the *Trigonometrical Survey* of England. That great work, highly creditable as it is to the individuals by whom it is conducted, has already been thirty-three years in progress, and yet it still wants one-third part of its completion. It ought to be added, however, that the operations of the Ordnance suffered interruption during the war."

Colby, who succeeded Mudge in 1820, carried out the Irish Survey, which was completed in 1846, the year of his retirement. The old methods, once used by Roy in Scotland, of pacing, or by Mudge in his earliest county sheets, of perambulating, had given way to accurate measurement, the great triangle with its base on Lough Foyle enabling smaller triangles to be constructed, and the latter to be broken up into lines that were actually measured with a chain. Two thousand men were employed upon the Irish Survey, and the cost was about £800,000. Colby carried out the work well : in addition to the survey itself, he compiled " Memoirs " or information of all sorts about the country, most of which, however, were never printed, and remain in manuscript in Dublin.

It is to Colby that the high standards of Ordnance Survey work are largely due. Before he undertook the Irish Survey, he founded a school in Wales for the men who were to be engaged in it. His regulations demanded very particular accuracy and careful checking, beyond anything that had been required earlier. His staff grumbled, an official enquiry was held, and the regulations were made easier, and some of the work was placed out to contract. He himself wrote a few months later : " To my great regret I found that the contract plans had, in very few instances, possessed the original accuracy which would have fitted them to form the kind of map which was required by the country. My original instructions were again considered and restored into complete operation." And so they have been ever since.

So far, in the British Isles, then, we had a 2-inch survey of England below the Hull–Preston line, reduced to 1-inch printed maps, a 6-inch survey of Ireland, and Roy's old manuscript maps of Scotland. It was natural that the success of the Irish Survey should lead to a demand that Great Britain should also be mapped on the 6-inch scale, allowing the series of Mudge's maps to continue by making a reduction to 1 inch from it.

Thus began what was called the Battle of the Scales. The proposal for a British 6-inch map cut across the business of the private land surveyors, who had to be called in whenever there was a proposal to build a canal, railway, or road, or whenever alterations had to be made to an estate. Private surveyors had not the ability to erect beacons, or the staff to use the elaborate methods of the Ordnance Survey, or to publish their final maps, while no two surveyors worked on the same system. Early Ordnance Survey reports say :

" Enormous sums of money have been expended upon surveys for railways and on plotting fields . . . in the employment of surveyors at 5 and 10 guineas a day ; " and " This enormous competition for surveyors and draughtsmen, who are under no central control, raises the price far beyond that of any national Survey."

As an example from a day before the railway mania which drove surveying costs beyond reason, we may give (see page 118) an extract from the accounts, published in 1805, of the Ellesmere Canal, of expenses incurred to that date, most of which would have been avoided if a large-scale plan had been in existence.

The root of the trouble is stated in another Ordnance report : " . . . there is a vast number of persons, such as local surveyors, who are interested and do not wish to put into the hands of individuals maps which will give them all the information which generally is only to be obtained through surveyors."

However, the Government won the battle, and the 6-inch survey was continued up to the Border, and a 1-inch reduction made from it. This latter was known for a time as the cadastral 1-inch, the word cadastral coming from the Latin

Surveys, Plans, Reference Books, Application to Land-Owners, Surveyors and Engineers attending Parliament, and valuing Land.

———

	£	s.	d.
John Duncombe, for salary in making surveys, sections, plans, attending Parliament, and acting as resident engineer to the Company, from 1791 to June 30, 1803, including all travelling and other expenses allowed him......	4402	2	5
Davies and Jebb, land surveyors, for making original plans and books of reference, also the subsequent ones, attending Parliament at sundry times, valuing land and damages during the execution of the work, and making plans of the Canal as completed, including expenses....................	3010	9	10
William Jessop, for sundry surveys, journies, inspections, plans, estimates, and for attending Parliament at several times, including his expenses.........	1103	18	0
Joseph Turner, for surveys	44	15	6
William Turner, for ditto..............	763	5	10½
Andrews, for plans, paid by Mr. Potts ...	21	6	3
Calveley . . . ditto....................	13	15	0
John Howell, for sundry surveys, plans, and attending Parliament . . . also making surveys of the line from Weston to Shrewsbury	216	12	11
To sundry persons, paid by Thomas Telford, as per his accounts	203	6	0
John Fletcher	53	19	0
Thomas Denson, a gratuity, per order of the Committee in 1795............ •	5	5	0
	£9838	15	9½

capitastrum, and indicating a connection with taxation, presumably because the original Irish 6-inch had been made for valuation purposes, and therefore the 6-inch became associated with taxation.

For the northern maps, however, only one meridian was used, that passing through Delamere Forest (though, of course, the calculations of position, such as degrees and minutes east or west, was on Greenwich meridian, as in all Ordnance maps, and the Delamere meridian was used in order to minimise the distortion from the projection), and the sheets, 36 inches by 24 inches, were published in quarter sheets, 18 inches by 12 inches. Kent, Essex, Surrey, and Sussex had been first issued in small bound folios, one for each county, and the remainder in sheets that were all 23 inches from north to south, but were between 29 inches and 34 inches east to west. The sheets were at first published without the hachuring, owing to the delay in making the hill sketches upon which it was based, and they were numbered in continuation of Mudge's sheets.

When the Border was reached, in 1870, it was decided to re-do the southern sheets so as to bring England and Wales on to one meridian, and then all the sheets were re-numbered from the north. The final number was 357, though there were only 354 sheets of this " *New Series* ", which constituted the second edition.

Scotland, which followed, was not made on the Cassini projection which had been used for England and Wales, but on the new Bonne projection which had been used for the French survey on the 1/80,000 scale. Not until 1932 did all the 1-inch maps of Great Britain fall into line with one another. There were 131 sheets of the Scottish 1-inch, each 18 inches by 24 inches.

Engraving on copper was still employed in the production, but photo-zincography had been used as a method of hurrying the production of the maps when the engravers got behind with their work. By this process the original drawing is transferred to a prepared zinc plate from which the printing is done. These maps were only a stopgap, however, and the copper-plate editions were issued as soon as they were ready.

So far all maps had been black and white, but by 1900 Great Britain was covered by a 1-inch series in black and brown. These had come about because the alterations that were all the time being made to the copper-plates to keep them up-to-date injured the hachures, and so the hachuring was put on a different plate from the rest of the map, and printed in brown.

Towards the end of the nineteenth century two further developments took place in the 1-inch map. The original had been made on a plan designed to make sure that the whole country was mapped in the shortest time, and no regard was paid to the tourist uses to which the maps would be put, or to their value in administration by local authorities. It often happened that a particular tourist area was found on the corner of four maps, while the map edges might run through the middle of a town. It was therefore decided to produce district maps, and there are now a very large number of these available.

The second development was to increase colour. There were two forms of the Third Edition of the 1-inch, the first being a black-and-white edition, omitting hachures and showing contours instead. The second, " fully-coloured ", series was printed by lithography, the transfers being made from the copper-plates to the stone, and a different stone being used for each colour, of which there were six.

The hachures were preserved, and were printed in a faint brown, while, in addition, contours in red were added. Water was in blue, roads in burnt sienna, and woods in green. The England and Wales series consisted of 152 sheets measuring 27 inches by 18 inches, but though the Scottish series conformed to the English colourings, the sheets were kept at the old size. A cover was now provided for the folded sheets of this edition, which was completed in 1912.

Experiments were now made for the Fourth Edition, and H. S. L. Winterbotham speaks especially of the " Killarney " sheet, in thirteen printings, and an experimental sheet of Somerset. Then came the 1914–18 war, and when it was over economy was the rule in all Government enterprises. The fourth or " Popular " edition therefore used the old copper-plates, which were cut up and rejoined so as to make the sheets more convenient for the traveller. Hachures were abandoned, and in addition to the 100-foot contours which had been surveyed, the new series showed interpolated con-

SECTION OF THE FIRST ORDNANCE SURVEY.

tours at every 50 feet. This was done in order to help give a mental picture of the country, especially where it was flat : the interpolated contours were put in from sketches made on the ground.

There were now seven colours : black, two different blues for water, green for woods, orange for contours, and red and brown for two different classes of roads. In addition, a black-and-white edition was published for those who use a map for special purposes and wish to apply their own colours. The sheets are 27 inches by 18 inches in size. The Scottish section of this fourth edition was produced from stone and zinc, and the originals were kept in the form of glass negatives, which could be touched up as required. The main advantage of abandoning copper-plate was that it enabled the production staff to use entirely new and more easily readable lettering, with more boldness than it is possible to get from engraving. The projection was altered to the Cassini, so that it now conformed to that of England and Wales, and an overlap of 1 inch, south and east, was added, so that there was no longer a difficult join to make between sheet and sheet. The size was that of the English sheets, with the overlap added.

Lastly, there is the present series, the fifth edition, made from the fourth revision in the field. There are two forms, one in relief, and one with the contours only ; the overlap, now of 2,000 yards, is maintained, and many new symbols are used for the new objects which now have to be mapped, such as power-lines. The full series is supplemented by district and special sheets.

Such is the history of the 1-inch map, which we have followed with care because it can be regarded as the basic map of our islands. There are, however, maps on other scales, of considerable interest, and each with its own uses.

$\frac{1}{10}$-*inch* (1 inch to 10 miles).

This was originally designed as an index to the old series of Mudge's maps, to show where the sheet lines fell and to indicate the different meridians. It was a reduction from the 1-inch. Not till 1902 was it published as a separate map, and then twelve sheets were produced covering Great Britain. The expansion of motoring increased its popularity, and in

1926 three sheets were published covering Great Britain, the map being layered to show the physical surface of the country, as well as showing contours. Of all the Ordnance maps it is perhaps the best from which to get easily an accurate idea of the geography of the whole island.

¼-*inch* (1 inch to 4 miles).

This also began as an index, and was completed as a reduction from the 1-inch to satisfy the demands of geologists. It was late in the nineteenth century before it was published for the public in both an outline and a coloured edition, and it still included some very old work.

After the 1914–18 war another edition was produced by lithography, except for the Kent sheet, which had been engraved before the war. In 1928 the sheet lines were altered and Ministry of Transport road-numbers were added, and a still later edition has traffic directions in the margin and town plans. There is also a civil air edition.

½-*inch* (1 inch to 2 miles).

At the beginning of the century Bartholemew produced a layered ½-inch which was a reduction from the 1-inch, and this led to the Ordnance Survey following. The map was drawn, with stamped names, and its forty sheets are issued in two editions, the one hill-shaded, the other layered.

6-*inch* (6 inches to the mile).

This, and its bigger brother the 25-inch, are usually called plans and not maps, though probably a plan to us brings up the idea rather than of a street plan in a town.

We have seen that the 1-inch was a reduction from a 6-inch field survey ; this latter was also published as it stood, and it covers Great Britain in 15,000 sheets. Contours, footpaths, and local boundaries, are shown, and it is a map that everyone should buy for his own neighbourhood, for it shows every feature of local interest, and one is astonished at the amount that can be learned from it about a locality that one had thought one knew well.

25-*inch* (25 inches to the mile).

In was in 1854 that the decision was made to map the whole country, except for the uncultivated Highland districts, on the 25-inch scale, which runs to 50,000 sheets. The decision to make a map on this scale was taken very soon after the 6-inch survey had started, because it was found that the latter was not large enough for all purposes. The 25-inch or 1/2500 scale has many advantages, the greatest being that one square inch on the map almost exactly equals an acre on the ground. It was decided at the same time to make plans of towns with over 4,000 people on the 1/500 scale.

These big plans, when they were first made, were used chiefly for Land Registration purposes—that is, for checking that land which was being bought and sold was the size and shape it was said to be, and also for purposes of valuation for rates and tithe ; but later on they proved useful for housing purposes, and maybe they have not yet exhausted their value.

The 25-inch plan shows all administrative boundaries, parish, rural district, Parliamentary, and so on ; in many cases the parish boundaries had never appeared on maps before, and had to be constructed with the help of the oldest inhabitants of the various villages. The boundaries of properties—that is, the amounts of land held by each owner—are not shown, but only public ones, and those that are natural, like hedges. The area of each piece of land, such as a field, is entered in the map, and the piece is given a number, which is recorded in the accompanying parish list. The figures of acreage were very easily got after a Sapper invented the " computing scale "—a sort of slide rule that adds up the number of small squares on tracing paper placed over the map. " By these computing scales we obtain the acreage to the hundredth part of an acre with a regularity which is perfectly astonishing : to those who have not seen it performed it would seem incredible." One is glad to know that the Sapper had 6d. a day added to his pay for the rest of his service as reward for his invention.

The 25-inch plan is not contoured, but instead it contains bench-marks and spot-heights. A bench-mark is placed at a particular spot on the countryside—it is often a stone in the wall of a house—and on it is recorded the height above sea-level. A bench-mark can be recognised easily enough, for it carries the broad arrow, the letters B.M., and the height above mean sea-level to the second place of decimals of a foot. A spot-height is a cairn or other recognisable spot marked on the map which can be identified on the ground, and in this case the height is recorded to the nearest foot.

Sea-level, by the way, is an expression which is not as simple in meaning as it sounds. In plans before 1929 sea-level was calculated from a line on the sea-wall at Liverpool which was thought to represent mean sea-level—that is, half-way between high and low tides; but as it was based on only a fortnight's observation, and as Liverpool is on a tidal river, it was found that the level was wrong. Newlyn in Cornwall (for England), and Dunbar in Scotland (for Scotland) were chosen, and the line was decided after hourly observations of the tide level over six years, 1915 to 1921. On plans published since 1929 it will be stated in the margin whether the heights are based on Newlyn or Liverpool, and if on Liverpool, then a plus or minus figure will show the amount to be added to or subtracted from shown heights to make them correct.

On these plans high- and low-water lines along the coast are shown, which were surveyed on dates midway between spring and neap tides, spring tides being those when the water rises highest and falls lowest, and neap tides those when there is the least difference between high and low tides. These lines are marked as H.W.M.O.T. (High-Water-Mark Ordinary Tide) and L.W.M.O.T. (Low-Water-Mark Ordinary Tide). In Scotland, however, the survey follows old customs and recording is done during spring tides. The letters H.W.M.O.S.T. (High-Water-Mark Ordinary Spring Tides) and L.W.M.O.S.T. (Low-Water-Mark Ordinary Spring Tides) will be found.

It is unfortunate that, owing to the 1914–18 war, the economy necessities of the peace, and the war of 1939, the work of revising the national plans has got farther and farther behind. The great housing development made it essential to survey the new estates and issue the plans, and areas where development had not been so rapid were neglected. The result of this policy of correcting a sheet here and there has been, for instance, that the areas of a piece of land that overlaps two sheets no longer correspond, for formerly the whole area of the piece was given on each plan, and now only the area of the piece that actually appears upon the plan; again, the numbers of the pieces of land have got very involved, and the parish lists out of date. One can only hope that in future more money will be granted to the Ordnance Survey so that these plans, the basis of all our maps, may be kept more nearly up to date than has so far been possible.

1/M (1 inch to 15·782 miles).

This map, on the scale of 1/1,000,000, is the British section of an international map which arose out of a meeting of the International Geographical Congress at Geneva in 1908, after which, on the suggestion of Sir Charles Close, Director-General of the Ordnance Survey, the British Government invited representatives from other countries to a conference in London in 1909 to draw up the necessary conventions.

The sheets themselves cover 6° of longitude by 4° of latitude, and thus the map-size varies, becoming smaller nearer the poles. Heights are layered, and contours shown. Each sheet was produced by the country that had the largest amount of territory in the area to be mapped. The seven sheets into which the British Isles fall have been joined up into two sheets by the Ordnance Survey.

Of the making of maps there is no end. Unceasingly and universally, explorers, surveyors, naturalists and other specialists quarter the globe from pole to pole collecting information, discovering new features and correcting old errors; while draughtsmen, photographers and colourists plot, print and produce the finished article. In the preparatory stages the Royal Geographical Society plays a leading part—not only in organising systematic procedure and in stimulating interest in original research, but also in providing funds or equipment, or both, to qualified explorers when such assistance is justified.

Those of our readers who may wish to study the creative side of mapping will find a rich mine of information in the *Monthly Record of Geography*, published under the authority of the Council of the Royal Geographical Society. Bound volumes of these proceedings may generally be seen in most public libraries.

CHAPTER ELEVEN

CHARTS

A CHART is a sea-map upon which the navigator can see the lie of the sea-bed beneath the water, and know the depth and movements of the sea, and which will enable him to find his way from one port to another. Before charts existed or were as accurate as they are now, a mariner learned by experience alone, and the knowledge that he had stored up over many years of sailing he passed on to his son ; yet even now a chart is very different from a map. Shoals come and go, submarine explosions thrust up new rocks and pull down others, and there is nothing to tell the navigator that an alteration has occurred until a ship strikes upon an uncharted rock. Even to-day large areas of the Arctic and Antarctic seas have never been charted, while there are many unexplored depths in all the oceans of the world.

It was in the Middle Ages that we find the first charts, and they grew up from the great sea-trade that was being brought into being in the Mediterranean by the cities of Italy and Catalonia (that part of Spain lying between the River Ebro and the Pyrenees). Part of this trade grew out of the activity that followed upon the Crusades, in bringing to the West the gold and the new articles of merchandise of the Saracens part was due to the decay in Italy of the feudal system and the growth of semi-independent towns free to manage their own affairs. These grew rapidly when they were no longer under the control of Duke or Lord, and were encouraged by the Emperors for the taxes they yielded. Such were the causes of the trade, but that the ships which carried goods between Barcelona, Genoa, Pisa, Venice, and the other cities of the Mediterranean were able to navigate the open sea safely with their valuable cargoes was due to the discoveries that led in the fourteenth century to the invention of the mariner compass.

In Roman times the sailors of the Empire had books called *peripli* which were collections of sailing directions, giving them instructions for following the coast from one port to another and information about anchorages and current Without the compass, and with only the sun and stars to guide

hem, these early sailors did not venture far from land except
vhen they had to. The first *periplus* appeared about the time
of Alexander the Great, and described the whole circuit of the
Mediterranean. These *peripli* developed into the portolan
books that were used in the early Middle Ages.

The date of the earliest charts is not known, but Guillaume
le Nangis describes the crusade that King Louis IX made in
270, and says that during the voyage from Aiguesmortes in
France to Cagliari in Sardinia, which had been appointed the
meeting-place for the ships of the Crusade, a storm came up,
and at the end of the sixth day the king asked the exact
position of the ship; so the pilots brought their charts to him
and showed him that the port was not far away.

The earliest of the portolan charts, as they were called, that
exists to-day is dated 1311, and from that date they became
more and more frequent. Before 1500 they did not bear upon
them the lines of latitude and longitude, and they were never
constructed upon a projection, but were the result of careful
measurement, and were so accurate that it is not until comparatively recent times that they were at last improved upon.
Whereas in many sixteenth-century maps the error in the
length of the Mediterranean is nearly 20°, in the charts it
seldom exceeds 1°. These charts, built out of the experience,
century after century, of sea-captains, seamen, and map-
makers, are all different, and yet all are made on a common
plan, and all, as far as we can see, with a common ancestor, for
they show a strong sense of tradition. They show the
Mediterranean, with varying amounts of the Atlantic and
West African coasts, usually as far as Cape Finisterre in the
north and Cape Bojador in the south, while in the east are
shown the Black Sea and part of the Red Sea.

One of the things one notices at once about these charts is
the network of lines that crosses them. At various points on
the chart, selected for no reason at all that one can see, are
crossing points where all these lines intersect, and as the
charts become more elaborate and decorated, so these points
or wind-roses become more ornamented; at the same time
towns are indicated by little pictures, and large flags or coats-
of-arms mark states. The authorities differ about what these
lines were originally meant to convey: it is probable that they
began as lines showing the directions of the wind, and later

became, as Mr. G. Herbert Fowler's book on Charts has it
" diagonal lines drawn from port to port which cut al
meridians at the same angle (and) gave the approximately tru
course, and were termed loxodromes, the word meanin
' slanting-course ' lines ; radiating ' compasses ' drawn al
over the chart enabled the mariner to set his course at and t
any point by aid of the magnetic needle ".

Those who are interested in these lovely charts can se
reproductions in *Portolan Charts*, by E. L. Stevenson, or ii
Periplus, by A. E. Nordenskiöld.

The making of charts soon gravitated to the same countr
that was producing great map-makers, Holland, and it is
craft associated with a man who had served in the Dutcl
merchant service as a boy, and became a well-known an
respected pilot, Janszoon Wagenar. The famous printin
firm of Plantin published his first atlas, with twenty-thre
charts engraved on copper and many pages of information
in 1584, and this number was soon afterwards increased t
forty-four.

After the destruction of the Spanish Armada, England'
navy sailed supreme as the ruler of the waves, and it was hig
time that our sailors should be provided with charts of ou
home waters. Anthony Ashley, secretary of the Treasur
having obtained the consent of the Privy Council, commis
sioned Wagenar to make a set of eight charts of the coastlin
from Aberdeenshire to Land's End, the sailing directions bein
translated into English, from the Dutch text, by Ashley himsel

The author's name became in England corrupted t
Waggoner, and the book was known as a " Waggoner "
Pepys, who was Secretary to the Navy under Charles II
wrote in his diary on July 22, 1663 : " Thence to my book
seller's and found my Waggoners done. The very bindin
cost be 14/- but they are well done and so with a porter hom
with them " ; and on September 19th, 1666, " Mightil
troubled even in my sleep at my missing four or five of m
biggest books, Speed's chronicle and maps and the two part
of Waggoner which I suppose I have put up with too much car
that I have forgot where they are for sure they are not stole.

Meanwhile, on the Continent, Blaeu was improving upo
Wagenar's work. John Blaeu, in his *Atlas* of 1664, referrin
to the charts of Wagenar and his successor Barentszoen, said

WAGENAR'S CHART OF THE THAMES ESTUARY.

" My late father not only greatly improved both of these, but also enlarged them for the benefit of navigation, adding to them so much that was lacking that his may justly be called a new work." He was referring to the chart-atlas of Blaeu senior published in 1621, and called *The Light of Navigation in which are plainly drawn and described all the Coasts & Harbours of the Western, Northern, Eastern & Mediterranean Seas Also many countries, islands and places of Guinea, Brazil, East & West Indies. Partly taken from the works of the best writers on marine matters (as Lucas Jansz. Waghenaer and others) but improved through the writings of experienced seamen, and by making use of their statements and explanations . . .*, and to a further volume called *The Mirror of the Sea*, in 1627.

In thinking of the use that seamen made of charts at that time, we must remember that while they could calculate latitude, they had no instrument for the accurate calculation of longitude, and as the ship's log was not invented till about 1650 and did not become common till later, speed was estimated from the size and number of the sails, a guess as to the strength of the wind, or timing a piece of wood as it passed the length of the ship.

Many famous names follow Wagenar, and precede the setting up of the Hydrographic Office of the Admiralty in 1795, but of them three deserve special mention.

Sir Robert Dudley's sea-atlas, *Dell' Arcano del Mare*, published in 1646/7, is remarkable as being the first in which the charts are drawn on Mercator's projection, and for the statement of the engraver (Antonio Francesco Lucini) that he worked on the plates in a Tuscan village for twelve years, and used 5000 lb. of copper. Charts are still in most cases drawn on Mercator's projection, which has proved itself the best for purposes of navigation.

John Seller published from 1671 to 1675 *The English Pilot*, describing the Northern, Southern and Oriental Navigations, though the last was never finished. He followed this with *The Coasting Pilot, describing the Sea Coasts, Channels, Soundings . . . upon the Coasts of England, Flanders and Holland*, in 1680, and a pocket *Atlas Maritimus* in 1682. Seller dealt in maps, charts, and geographical books, from his shop At the Sign of the Mariner's Compass, at Hermitage Stairs, Wapping (there is still a Great Hermitage Street in Wapping, and a

I

Hermitage Basin in the London Docks), where his customers would be most easily found. His son moved to Cheapside, but continued to sell his father's works.

Atlantic Neptune, which was compiled by Des Barres and published by the Board of Admiralty during the seven years 1774–1781, for the use of the Royal Navy in American waters, is the most extensive and elaborate series of sea-charts in existence. The peculiar shape of the volumes—so long and of so little depth—is accounted for by the exigencies of space in the cabin-lockers of that period. This accurate and highly artistic work has been described by Rich as " The most splendid collection of sea-charts ever published. It was executed at the expense of the British Government . . . and no expense appears to have been spared in order to render it a monument worthy of the nation."

Greenvile Collins was a naval captain who was ordered to chart the coasts, and who published the results as *Great Britain's Coasting Pilot* in 1693. These charts were the first original surveys to be made by an Englishman and printed ; the originals are preserved among the documents of the Chart Branch of the Hydrographic Office.

Based on the work of these and other men, a much more complete work in six parts, *The English Pilot*, appeared in many editions between the years 1743 and 1761, and this set divides the days that look back to the portolan charts and Wagenar from those that look forward to modern times.

In 1795 the Hydrographic Office of the Admiralty was set up under Alexander Dalrymple, and from it has developed the present organisation, which, in addition to the Chart Branch, covers Sailing Directions, Tides, Lights Lists, Notices to Mariners, etc. It was at first separate from the Surveying Service, and was formed to take custody of charts and to compile information useful to the navigation of H.M. Ships. The staff comprised three people ; even in 1813, when the Surveying Service was supervised by the Hydrographer, it numbered only seven. The Department now has a personnel of 1,100. The first catalogue of Admiralty Charts contained 736 ; to-day there are about 3,700.

The basis of a chart is the practical surveying work on the spot undertaken by the specialists in the Surveying Service of the Navy.

There are three types of survey : Ocean, Coastal, and Harbour. The first is well out of sight of land, usually in very deep water, and is on a small scale. Positions are found astronomically by the sun, the moon, and the stars. The coastal survey is made for the benefit of ships navigating near, though possibly out of sight of, land. It is usually on a scale of about 1 inch, $\frac{3}{4}$ inch, or $\frac{1}{2}$ inch to the mile. The harbour survey is made on a much bigger scale, sometimes as much as 30 inches to the mile, and covers harbours and anchorages where a ship will want to know very exactly her position and be able to see a picture of the land in far greater detail.

The coastal and harbour surveys are based upon the same principles of triangulation used in a land survey. A number of intervisible points, such as mountain summits, church towers, or the tops of cliffs or islands, are selected. At these points, known as Main Stations, a theodolite is set up, and all the angles of the Main Triangulation are observed very carefully. If the distance between two points is known, then the distance between any other points can be calculated by trigonometry. If not, a Base has to be measured with a steel tape to the nearest thousandth part of an inch. The exact position in latitude and longitude of one Main Station (and from it all the other Main Stations can be calculated) is also required. If it is known, well and good ; if not, it will have to be found very carefully by means of an Astrolabe, an instrument with which observations of the stars are made in conjunction with a Chronograph, another instrument that measures time (or longitude) to the thousandth part of a second. When a survey is completed these Main Stations are marked, perhaps by a brick buried in the ground, or a triangle scratched on a lead roof or on the surface of a rock, so that in the future, if a chart requires revision, a surveyor may go to the exact spot, and need not go through another lengthy and complicated Main Triangulation.

A large sheet of strong paper, known as the Plotting Sheet, is then taken, and the Main Stations and the graduation of the latitude and longitude are plotted upon it. In some surveys it may be necessary to have a Secondary Triangulation within the framework of the Main Triangulation.

Marks consisting of flags or whitewashed patches on the rocks are put up along the coast ; these and all prominent landmarks, such as chimneys, church spires, lighthouses, and

other objects which can be seen at a great distance, are observed
from the Main and Secondary Stations by theodolite or
sextant, and are plotted on the Plotting Sheet. The greatest
care is taken with all the work that goes on the Plotting Sheet,
as this is the basis of the survey. All the Stations and marks
are plotted by at least three lines, which must intersect in a
point when seen under a magnifying glass. If they do not
meet in a point, the plotting must be done again. The
intersecting point is then pricked through with a needle. The
number of marks required depends upon the size of the survey
and the configuration of the land ; it must be possible for the
ship and the boats to fix their position accurately anywhere in
the area to be surveyed.

It may happen that part of the survey, or even perhaps
all of it, may include an area that is out of sight of land, or so
far off that it is not possible to get an accurate fix from the
shore-marks. In such a case floating beacons carrying large
flags are anchored or moored at regular intervals. Generally
at least two of these beacons are fixed very accurately from
the shore, and another triangulation of the beacons is made
in much the same way as the Main or Secondary Triangulation
on shore. But since the beacons are floating, and therefore
move with the tide, it is not possible to attain such accuracy
as on land. The positions of the beacons are also plotted on
the Plotting Sheet.

A large sheet of tracing paper is then placed over the
Plotting Sheet, and all the marks and graduation are pricked
through with a needle, so that a perfect replica of the Plotting
Sheet is made. All the marks required in any particular
portion of the survey are then transferred by needle-point on
to the Field-boards and Sounding-boards, which are ordinary
drawing-boards covered with strong paper on which all the
work is done. The survey is then ready to begin.

A chart is made for the safe navigation of ships. The most
important and by far the greater part of the survey is the
sounding. This is done partly by the Surveying Ship herself
and partly by the boats she carries. The boats sound inshore
and on the shoals where it would be dangerous for the ship to
work. Lines, usually $\frac{1}{10}$ inch apart, are drawn on the Sounding-boards, along which the ship and boats steam, sounding
the whole time and fixing at frequent intervals. The fixing is

SECTION OF ADMIRALTY CHART OF THE THAMES ESTUARY.
(In the actual chart all lights are printed in orange.)
(By permission of H.M. Stationery Office and the Hydrographer of the Navy.)

done by taking two simultaneous angles with Sextants between three of the fixed marks on shore or the beacons. These angles are then set on the Station Pointers, which are coaxed into the only position in which each leg cuts the centre of the prick-hole of the mark. The centre of the Station Pointers is then on the position at which the fix was taken. These fixed positions are ringed round in pencil and numbered consecutively. All the fixes and all the soundings are recorded in a book, so that it is possible to re-plot any part of the survey if it should be necessary at some future date.

A ship which moves about the sea requires to know what is the least water that she can expect to find under her bottom in any particular place. The chart will tell her this, because the soundings show the depth of water below the level of Mean Low Water at Spring Tides. But the surveying ship and her boats must work throughout the day ; the soundings that they take are therefore corrected for the height of the tide, which is measured every day at half-hourly intervals on a Tide Pole. At the end of each day when the ship anchors and the boats return the soundings are reduced to the level of Mean Low Water Springs, and are inked-in on the Sounding-boards. Depths are sometimes shown in feet, but are usually in fathoms and feet (a fathom is 6 feet), indicated by two figures, the larger being the number of fathoms and the smaller the number of feet between it and the next fathom ; *e.g.* 3_5 represents 3 fathoms 5 feet, or 23 feet. Contour lines for 1, 3, 6, 10, 20, 50, and 100 fathoms are drawn as the survey progresses.

The lines of soundings are always run at right angles to the general run of the fathom contours so that a sudden shoal will not be missed. When the soundings have been inked-in it is decided whether or not a shoal requires further examination. If it does, additional lines of soundings, or " interlines ", are run between the main lines. If the shoal is rocky it may be necessary to run many lines crossing and recrossing it, so that it is certain that the least water on top of it has been obtained.

In the old days soundings in shallow water up to 10 fathoms were taken with the hand lead-line ; in deeper water special machines, with wire in place of the lead line, were used, the wire passing round the circumference of a dial which recorded the amount that had gone out. Both these methods are still practised to-day, although they have been almost entirely superseded by the echo-sounding machine, which can be employed not only in shallow water but also in the ocean where depths of 2,000 and 3,000 fathoms can be recorded. Deep-sea sounding with the lead is a very laborious process ; it takes more than half an hour for the lead to reach the bottom in 2,000 fathoms and over an hour to haul it up again. But it is still in use, not only for sounding but also for taking samples of the bottom ; and at the same time that a deep-sea sounding is being taken, another machine is used for lowering a specially constructed water-bottle for taking samples and temperatures of the ocean at various depths. Scientists require to know the salinity and temperature of the ocean, and also what the bottom is composed of.

The echo-sounding machine sends out a sonic signal (or super-sonic—that is, a sound signal whose vibrations are so rapid that it cannot be heard by the human ear) either by an automatic hammer tapping on the ship's bottom or by an electric impulse. This signal is directed downwards to the sea-bed, which reflects it back again to hydrophones in the ship. In the machine a revolving stylus makes a mark on a roll of paper when the signal is sent out and again when it is received back again. The reception line thus draws a perfect picture of the undulations of the sea-bottom below the line of the ship's path.

There is great saving of time with the echo-sounding machine, especially in deep water. Not only does it record all the shoals, some of which might be missed by the lead, but it may tell the surveyor more about the bottom than will the lead. For instance, it will tell him how thick a layer of mud may be when it is lying on top of rock, for an echo is obtained from the surface of the mud and from the surface of the rock. But it will not tell him what is the nature of the sea-bed—that is, if it is shingle or gravel or sand. The seaman requires to know not only how much water there is under his ship, but also what the bottom is composed of. If he must anchor his ship, he will not choose a rocky bottom, because the anchor will not grip. If he has any choice, he will anchor in mud, for that is the best holding ground. While the soundings are being taken during the course of the survey, samples of the sea-bed are also taken at regular intervals. This is done by

" arming " the lead with tallow or soft soap, which, when it strikes the bottom, picks up a small amount of material. An abbreviated description of the bottom is inked-in on the Sounding-board in the appropriate place. Thus, f. sk. S.b.M. would mean " fine speckled Sand and black Mud ".

Although the greater part of a survey is the sounding, a certain amount of work is done on shore. The coastline—that is, the High Water Mark of Spring Tides—has to be drawn in, which means that the surveyor has to walk along its length, fixing himself at frequent intervals, and noting the character of the shore both above High Water Mark and below it. The navigator when approaching a coast will require to know what the land looks like—whether it is mountainous or flat, cliffs or sand-dunes. Usually, if the land has been well surveyed, the surveyor takes the topography from the land maps (in the case of the British Isles from the 6-inch Ordnance Survey maps), but if he is in an out-of-the-way part of the world, he may have to do the topography himself.

At the end of the surveying season the ship lies up at her base, and during the ensuing four months the " Fair Sheet " is drawn for as many of the surveys as have been done during the season. This is pricked through from the Plotting Sheet for the graduation and the Main Secondary Stations and Sound-ing-marks. The soundings, coastline, and topography are traced from small tracings not more than a foot square (to reduce paper distortion) which were brought up to date at the end of each week during the season. The topography of the Fair Sheet is drawn in colours and the soundings are in black Indian ink. Some sheets may have as many as 50,000 soundings. When the drawing is finally completed the Fair Sheet is checked with the tracings from which the chart was drawn and with the Collector Tracing (that is the ship's copy of the Fair Sheet, which was brought up to date weekly during the survey), both of which have been previously checked with the Sounding- and Field-boards.

The Fair Sheet is then sent to the Hydrographic Depart-ment of the Admiralty. First it is given a thorough and detailed examination by the cartographers, who then prepare from it a tracing, perhaps on a reduced scale, which will be the model from which the engravers work. The coastline, topography, and the fathom contours are taken direct from

the Fair Sheet ; but the Fair Sheet has many more soundings
on it than are required by the navigator, and most of these
have to be discarded by the cartographers. This is done by a
system of dividing the Fair Sheet into squares. The smallest
sounding on the shoals is taken, and then one representative
sounding from each square is selected so that an even pattern
of soundings is obtained, the soundings being sufficiently
close to tell the navigator that the chart has been well surveyed
and yet far enough apart to allow him to navigate without
being confused by the number of soundings.

The lettering on the charts is done in a uniform way for
ease in reading, a number of different styles being employed,
each style being used for certain types of names. For
instance, the lettering referring to land-names is different from
that referring to sea-names. Dangers such as rocks and shoals
are shown in the clearest kind of lettering.

When the tracing has been completed by the cartographers
it is very carefully checked with the Fair Sheet and with the
Sailing Directions (which have been brought up to date during
the survey), and any discrepancies are eliminated. Information about tides is inserted in a table in a corner of the chart,
and compass roses are added. When completed and checked
it is sent to the engravers.

Charts were first engraved on copper in the sixteenth
century, and this medium is still used to-day. There are
certain disadvantages ; for instance, the engraving must be
done by hand, which is a slow process, and the charts are
" pulled " through the presses by hand ; in course of time the
copper plates become distorted. But the great advantage of
copper, which outweighs all the disadvantages, is that when a
chart requires correction the copper can be burnished to
obliterate the old engraving and then re-engraved, or a piece
of the plate may even be cut out and a new piece inserted.
In the case of land-maps, once the map is printed the changes
over a course of years are seldom sufficient to require a new
edition ; but charts need constant correction because sand-
banks shift, buoys and lightships may be relaid in different
positions, wrecks must be charted, new dangers are discovered ;
and the mariner must have at his disposal all the latest available
information in order that he may navigate his ship in safety.

By using the copper plate as a " negative ", charts can be
printed by means of lithography on stone or zinc, which is

cheaper, and the copper plate has a much longer life before it begins to distort.

Amendments to charts are published in Weekly Notices to Mariners. These are small corrections which can be made by the navigator himself. They sometimes include reproductions of newly surveyed portions of a chart which can be pasted in the right position on a chart that is already in use. These amendments may be the result of the work of the surveying ships, but they are often made from information supplied by harbour boards and other authorities all over the world. In addition, information comes from charts made by foreign Governments, which are obtained by exchange through the International Hydrographic Bureau, and from ships of the Navy and the Merchant Service, which send in any information that may be of interest to the department.

Any reader who loves the sea will borrow (through his public library) or buy the Catalogue of Admiralty Charts, which lists every chart, and shows at the back a series of maps illustrating the limits of each chart that is available. There is excitement in the very names on the list. Do we not remember Drake, not to speak of Captain Blood, as we read such details as the following :—

Chart No.	Title.	Scale, inches to mile.	Natural scale.	Date of publication.	New edition or large correction.	Size, inches.
1519	Entrance to Laguna de Maracaibo :			Apr. 1934		41 × 24
	Outer Bar to Inner Bar (Barra Tablazo)	2·4	30,000		—	
	Inner Bar or Barra Tablazo	2·4	30,000			
	Outer Bar to La Ceiba	0·2	300,000			
	San Lorenzo	9·7	7,500			
	La Ceiba	9·7	7,500			
396	Cabo La Vela to Chagres, with the southern coast showing the Gulf of Panama	0·07	985,000	Oct. 1892	July 1929	38 × 25
	Puerto Carreto	1·0	72,600			
	Port Cispata	0·5	151,000			
	Santa Marta	3·0	24,000			
	Puerto Covenas	2·9	25,000			
2259	Puerto Columbia (Savanilla harbour)	2·8	25,700	Dec. 1894	Oct. 1929	26 × 19
	Puerto Columbia pier	7·0	10,400			
	Rio Magdalena	1·1	64,200			
2434	Puerto Cartagena	2·5	29,000	Apr. 1856	Nov. 1935	44 × 25
	Boca Chica or little entrance to Puerto Cartagena	10·0	7,300			

So, through 700 years, has grown the science that works still to make the seas safer for the ships of commerce, of war, and of pleasure, and gives information alike to the masters of the largest liners and the smallest sea-going yachts.

BOOKS

Map-making.

BRYANT, V. SEYMOUR, and HUGHES, T. H., *Map Work*.
DEBENHAM, FRANK, *Map Making*.
ELLES, GERTRUDE L., *The Study of Geological Maps*.
GARNETT, W., *A Little Book on Map Projection*.
ENCYCLOPÆDIA BRITANNICA. Articles on *Maps* and *Charts*.

History of Maps.

CHUBB, T., *The Printed Maps in the Atlases of Great Britain and Ireland*.
— *A Descriptive List of the Printed Maps of Somersetshire, 1575–1914*.
CLOSE, SIR CHARLES, *The Map of England*.
FORDHAM, SIR GEORGE, *Maps, their History, Characteristics and Uses*.
— *An Address on the Evolution of the Maps of the British Isles*.
— *Studies in Carto-Bibliography*.
— *Christopher Saxton of Dunningley*.
H.M. STATIONERY OFFICE, *The National Plans*.
HUMPHREYS, A. L., *Old Decorative Maps and Charts*.
SHEARER, J. E., *Old Maps and Map-Makers of Scotland*.
STEVENSON, E. L., *Willem Janszoon Blaeu, 1571–1638*.
SYNGE, *A Book of Discovery*.
WINTERBOTHAM, H. S. L., *A Key to Maps*.

Charts.

FOWLER, G. HERBERT, *Charts : their Use and Meaning*.
HAYES, GERALD R., *The Production of an Admiralty Chart*.
NORDENSKIÖLD, A. E., *Periplus*.
POTTER, J. D. (publisher), *Catalogue of Admiralty Charts and Other Hydrographic Publications*.
— *British Admiralty Charts and other Hydrographic Publications—their Use and Correction*.
SOMERVILLE, VICE-ADMIRAL BOYLE, *The Chart-Makers*.
STEVENSON, E. L., *Portolan Charts*.

INDEX